NEW Keystone

WORKBOOK

B

NEW
Keystone B

Workbook

Copyright © 2019 by Pearson Education, Inc.

All rights reserved. No part of this publication may be reproduced, stored in a retrieval system, or transmitted in any form or by any means, electronic, mechanical, photocopying, recording, or otherwise, without the prior permission of the publisher.

Pearson, 221 River Street, Hoboken, NJ 07030

Cover Credit: Miguel Sotomayor/Moment/Getty Images

Printed in the United States of America

ISBN-10: 0-13-523378-X
ISBN-13: 978-0-13-523378-8
73 2022
www.english.com/keystone

Contents

Unit 1

Reading 1
Vocabulary: Literary Words 1
Vocabulary: Academic Words 2
Word Study: Prefixes *in-, re-, over-, un-* 3
Reading Strategy: Predict 4
Comprehension 5
Response to Literature 5
Grammar: Adjectives after Indefinite Pronouns; Prenominal and Postnominal Adjectives . . . 6
Writing: Write a Description of an Object 8

Reading 2
Vocabulary: Key Words 9
Vocabulary: Academic Words 10
Word Study: Decoding Strategies: Digraphs 11
Reading Strategy: Preview for Main Idea and Details 12
Comprehension 13
Extension 13
Grammar: Subject-Verb Agreement: Non-count and Irregular-Plural Nouns; Comparison Structures 14
Writing: Write a Description of a Place 16

Reading 3
Vocabulary: Literary Words 17
Vocabulary: Academic Words 18
Word Study: Compound Nouns 19
Reading Strategy: Visualize 20
Comprehension 21
Response to Literature 21
Grammar: Simple Sentences: Consistent Forms, Parallel Structure; Adjectival Phrases: Adjective Order 22
Writing: Write a Description of a Person 24

Writing Workshop 25
Learning Log 26
Test Preparation 27
Visual Literacy: Smithsonian American Art Museum 31

Contents

Unit 2

Reading 1
Vocabulary: Literary Words 33
Vocabulary: Academic Words 34
Word Study: Roots *vict, laps, vis, mem, mand*. 35
Reading Strategy: Identify Problems and Solutions 36
Comprehension 37
Response to Literature. 37
Grammar: Simple Past: Regular and Irregular Verbs; Simple Sentences: Pronouns and Modifiers 38
Writing: Write a Story from a Different Point of View. 40

Reading 2
Vocabulary: Key Words 41
Vocabulary: Academic Words 42
Word Study: Words as Multiple Parts of Speech 43
Reading Strategy: Recognize Cause and Effect 44
Comprehension 45
Extension. 45
Grammar: More on Parallel Structure; Prepositions 46
Writing: Write a Story with a Starter 48

Reading 3
Vocabulary: Literary Words 49
Vocabulary: Academic Words 50
Word Study: Words Ending in *y*. 51
Reading Strategy: Make Inferences 52
Comprehension 53
Response to Literature. 53
Grammar: Complex Sentences with Adverbial Clauses of Time; Expressions of Quantity and Subject-Verb Agreement 54
Writing: Write a Personal Letter 56

Writing Workshop. 57
Learning Log. 58
Test Preparation 59
Visual Literacy: Smithsonian American Art Museum 63

Contents

Unit 3

Reading 1
Vocabulary: Key Words 65
Vocabulary: Academic Words 66
Word Study: Prefixes *under-*, *re-*, *multi-*, *inter-*. 67
Reading Strategy: Connect Ideas 68
Comprehension 69
Extension. 69
Grammar: Complex Sentences with Restrictive and Nonrestrictive Adjectival Clauses 70
Writing: Write a Compare-and-Contrast Paragraph 72

Reading 2
Vocabulary: Literary Words 73
Vocabulary: Academic Words 74
Word Study: Homophones 75
Reading Strategy: Identify Author's Purpose 76
Comprehension 77
Response to Literature. 77
Grammar: Gerunds as Subjects; Gerunds as Objects after Verbs and Prepositions 78
Writing: Write a Problem-and-Solution Paragraph 80

Reading 3
Vocabulary: Literary Words 81
Vocabulary: Academic Words 82
Word Study: Inflections *-ed* and *-ing* 83
Reading Strategy: Predict 2 84
Comprehension 85
Response to Literature. 85
Grammar: Infinitives; Clarifying with Appositives and Colons. 86
Writing: Write a News Article 88

Writing Workshop 89
Learning Log. 90
Test Preparation 91
Visual Literacy: Smithsonian American Art Museum 95

Contents

Unit 4

Reading 1
Vocabulary: Key Words 97
Vocabulary: Academic Words 98
Word Study: Related Words 99
Reading Strategy: Skim and Scan 100
Comprehension 101
Extension. 101
Grammar: Present Perfect; Conjunctive Adverbs 102
Writing: Write an Advertisement 104

Reading 2
Vocabulary: Key Words 105
Vocabulary: Academic Words 106
Word Study: Capitalizing Proper Nouns 107
Reading Strategy: Draw Conclusions 108
Comprehension 109
Extension. 109
Grammar: Compound and Complex Sentences; Agreement in Compound and Complex Sentences 110
Writing: Write a Persuasive Paragraph 112

Reading 3
Vocabulary: Literary Words 113
Vocabulary: Academic Words 114
Word Study: Spelling Long *e* 115
Reading Strategy: Summarize 116
Comprehension 117
Response to Literature 117
Grammar: Possessive Nouns and Adjectives; Antecedent-Pronoun and Subject-Verb Agreement 118
Writing: Write a Review 120

Writing Workshop 121
Learning Log 122
Test Preparation 123
Visual Literacy: Smithsonian American Art Museum 127

Contents

Unit 5

Reading 1
Vocabulary: Key Words 129
Vocabulary: Academic Words 130
Word Study: Synonyms 131
Reading Strategy: Make Generalizations 132
Comprehension 133
Extension 133
Grammar: Past Perfect: *had* + Past Participle; Compound and Complex Sentences with Past Perfect 134
Writing: Write a Cause-and-Effect Paragraph 136

Reading 2
Vocabulary: Key Words 137
Vocabulary: Academic Words 138
Word Study: Spelling *ie* / *ei* 139
Reading Strategy: Take Notes about Main Ideas and Key Details 140
Comprehension 141
Extension 141
Grammar: Imperatives and *will* for Instructions; Sequence Words, Phrases, and Clauses .. 142
Writing: Write an Instructional Paragraph 144

Reading 3
Vocabulary: Literary Words 145
Vocabulary: Academic Words 146
Word Study: Frequently Misspelled Words 147
Reading Strategy: Skim 148
Comprehension 149
Response to Literature 149
Grammar: Adjectival Phrases: Comparatives and Superlatives 150
Writing: Write a Classifying Paragraph 152

Writing Workshop 153
Learning Log 154
Test Preparation 155
Visual Literacy: Smithsonian American Art Museum 159

Contents

Unit 6
Reading 1
Vocabulary: Literary Words 161
Vocabulary: Academic Words 162
Word Study: Antonyms 164
Reading Strategy: Compare and Contrast 164
Comprehension 165
Response to Literature 165
Grammar: Reported Speech: Statements and Questions; Past Progressive with
   Adverbial Clauses 166
Writing: Write an Introductory Paragraph 168

Reading 2
Vocabulary: Key Words 169
Vocabulary: Academic Words 170
Word Study: Spelling Long *i* 171
Reading Strategy: Evaluate New Information 172
Comprehension 173
Extension 173
Grammar: Participial Adjectives: Formation and Meaning; Prepositions and Infinitives
   with Participial Adjectives 174
Writing: Write a Paragraph with a Main Idea and Supporting Details 176

Reading 3
Vocabulary: Key Words 177
Vocabulary: Academic Words 178
Word Study: Root Words 179
Reading Strategy: Evaluate Written Information 180
Comprehension 181
Extension 181
Grammar: Future for Prediction; Modals of Possibility and Advice;
   Punctuation of Direct Quotations; Quoting Sources 182
Writing: Write a Paragraph with Quotations and Citations 186

Writing Workshop 187
Learning Log 188
Test Preparation 189
Visual Literacy: Smithsonian American Art Museum 193

Name _____ Date _____

How does the natural world affect us?

Reading 1: "The Salmon People"

Vocabulary — **Literary Words** *Use with Student Edition page 5.*

REMEMBER Writers use **imagery** to create pictures in your mind. Imagery is created by sensory details. **Sensory details** tell you how something looks, sounds, smells, tastes, or feels.

Label each sentence with the sense it refers to: sight, sound, smell, taste, or touch.

Sense	Description
taste	The cup held a sour, salty liquid.
1.	A thick, sticky layer covered the surface.
2.	Red, blue, and yellow flowers danced in the wind.
3.	A deep, loud roar came from the engine.
4.	One muffin was especially sweet and delicious.
5.	The air was filled with the perfume of a thousand flowers.

Write a sentence with sensory details for each of the senses below.

Sense	Description
sound	He shut the door with a loud bang.
6. sight	
7. smell	
8. taste	
9. touch	
10. sound	

Unit 1 • Reading 1

1

Vocabulary **Academic Words** *Use with Student Edition page 6.*

Read the paragraph below. Pay attention to the underlined Academic Words.

> Announcement: Spring Celebration
> The town of Elmsburg celebrates the return of the birds to our nature preserve next Saturday, May 4. As several types of birds return from their southern <u>migration</u>, we welcome them with a birdwatching walk, games for children, and many opportunities to learn more about these birds and their life <u>cycles</u> from the experts. In the evening, stay for the annual barbecue, a yearly Elmsburg <u>tradition</u>. Native American storytelling rounds out the cultural activities. Don't miss this exciting <u>cultural</u> event!

Write the Academic Words from the paragraph above next to their correct definitions.

Example: __cultural__: reflecting the values and lifestyle of a group of people

1. _____: movement from one area to another

2. _____: something that is passed down from one generation to another

3. _____: a set of events that happen again and again

Use the Academic Words from the paragraph above to complete the sentences.

4. It's a _____ for the people in our town to have a big bonfire on the first day of winter.

5. I heard the geese flying south this morning in their seasonal _____.

6. The International Fair at school offered many different _____ foods.

7. The life _____ of a tree is seed, seedling, tree.

Complete the sentences with your own ideas.

Example: The life cycle of a butterfly is __egg, larva, pupa, butterfly__.

8. I have studied the migration patterns of _____.

9. My favorite cultural event in our town is _____.

10. Our school has a tradition of _____.

Name _____ Date _____

Word Study Prefixes *in-*, *re-*, *over-*, *un-* Use with Student Edition page 7.

REMEMBER A prefix is a letter or group of letters added to the beginning of a word to change its meaning. The prefix *in-* means "not," as in *inexact*. The prefix *re-* means "again," as in *replay*. The prefix *over-* means "too much," as in *overcooked*. The prefix *un-* means "not," as in *unfastened*.

Look at the chart. Add the prefix *in-*, *re-*, *over-*, or *un-* to each word in order to create a new word. Write the new word in the chart.

Word	Prefix	New Word	Definition
direct	in-	indirect	not direct
1. human	in-		
2. paint	re-		
3. use	over-		
4. lucky	un-		

Create a new word by adding the prefix *in-*, *re-*, *over-*, or *un-* to each word below. Then write the definition next to the new word. Check a dictionary if needed.

Examples: in- + distinct indistinct; not distinct, not clear

5. over- + flow _____

6. un- + wise _____

7. in- + formal _____

8. over- + eat _____

9. un- + ashamed _____

10. over- + sleep _____

Unit 1 • Reading 1

Reading Strategy | Predict

Use with Student Edition page 7.

> **REMEMBER** When you read, predict by asking yourself "What will happen next?" When you predict, look for clues in the story and illustrations, and think about what you already know about the topic.

Read the paragraphs and underline the clues that you can use to make a prediction.

1. Long ago, a native tribe in Canada <u>hunted deer and elk</u>. They were grateful for this food, but there were seasons when <u>they had very little to eat</u>. One day, the chief of the tribe <u>heard about a fish</u> called salmon.

   What do you think will happen next?

   The chief will try to find salmon for his tribe.

2. The chief sent four brothers to ask the sun, who told them where the salmon people lived—all the way to the sea. "Ask them politely," said the sun, "and they might send salmon to your river." The brothers prepared their canoes.

   What do you think will happen next?

   _____

3. The brothers paddled far into the west in search of the salmon people. At last, they came to an island with a small village near the shore. The friendly villagers introduced them to their chief, and the brothers gave the chief a gift.

   What do you think will happen next?

   _____

4. The chief ordered his people to prepare a feast. The brothers watched the young villagers walk to the edge of the sea, jump in, and return with salmon. After the feast, the chief said sternly, "You must now return each bone to the sea." One brother held onto a bone to see what would happen. The next time the young villagers went to catch fish, they didn't come back.

   What do you think will happen next?

   _____

5. The chief was very upset and asked his people to search for any missing bones in the sand. Feeling guilty, the brother who held the bone tossed it into the sea. Immediately, the young villagers returned with more fish. The chief promised to send salmon to their river as long as they returned all of the bones.

   What do you think will happen next?

   _____

Comprehension *Use with Student Edition page 12.*

Choose the *best* answer for each item. Circle the letter of the correct answer.

1. Bri thinks the first salmon ceremony is _____.

    a. boring
    b. strange
    c. exciting

2. The elder who tells the story of the salmon people says they must return _____ to the river.

    a. ashes
    b. drums
    c. bones

3. Sen worries that the salmon people will _____.

    a. be afraid
    b. forbid the feast
    c. never return

4. When the author uses the words *burning cedar wood and roasting salmon*, this sensory detail appeals to the sense of _____.

    a. smell
    b. touch
    c. sound

5. Bri hides the plastic bag in the back of her freezer to prove that the salmon people _____.

    a. don't care
    b. aren't real
    c. love her tribe

Response to Literature *Use with Student Edition page 13.*

Find a paragraph that you like very much in the story. Draw a picture illustrating the scene described in that paragraph in the box below.

Unit 1 • Reading 1

Grammar — Adjectives after Indefinite Pronouns

Use with Student Edition page 14.

> **REMEMBER** Indefinite pronouns, such as *something*, *anyone*, and *nowhere*, refer to something that is not specific. Adjectives usually come after indefinite pronouns.

Complete the chart with indefinite pronouns.

Indefinite Pronouns				
something	_____	somebody	_____	_____
_____	anyone	_____	anywhere	_____
_____	no one	_____	_____	no place

Complete each sentence with an indefinite pronoun from the chart above and the adjective in parentheses. Remember to use *any-* with negatives and questions.

Example: There is ___nothing worse___ than running out of gas. (worse).

1. Did you meet _____ at the party? (interesting)

2. I want to go _____ for vacation this year. (different)

3. He saw _____ in the sky yesterday. (bright)

4. I've never tasted _____ in my life than my aunt's cheesecake. (more delicious)

5. There is always _____ to do at Robert's house. (fun)

6. We never visit _____ on school trips. (unusual)

7. _____ than 15 can get on the ride. (older)

8. He hasn't seen _____ play basketball this year. (talented)

Name _____ Date _____

Grammar — Prenominal and Postnominal Adjectives

Use with Student Edition page 15.

> **REMEMBER** Adjectives are describing words. A prenominal adjective comes before the noun it describes.
> **Example:** small children
> A postnominal adjective comes after the noun it describes.
> **Example:** somewhere pretty
> In English, most adjectives are prenominal; postnominal adjectives often modify indefinite pronouns. Indefinite pronouns include words such as *something*, *somewhere*, and *someplace*.

Look at the adjectives and nouns. Circle the adjectives. Write *prenominal* if they come before a noun. Write *postnominal* if they come after a noun. The first one has been done for you.

Example: someplace (new) ___postnominal___

1. pretty dress _____
2. somewhere faraway _____
3. interesting book _____
4. something expensive _____
5. quick snack _____

Complete the sentences with an adjective from the box. If the nouns are indefinite pronouns, put the adjective after the noun. Otherwise, put the adjective before the noun.

| enormous | tiny | dry | frequent | bad |

6. (Modify *creatures*.) _____ can only be seen only through a microscope.

7. (Modify *something*.) If you are not careful when you drive, _____ may happen.

8. (Modify *insect*.) We saw an _____ in the backyard.

9. (Modify *rain*.) _____ keeps the forest alive and green.

10. (Modify *someplace*.) When we were caught in a storm, we tried desperately to find _____.

Unit 1 • Reading 1

Writing — Write a Description of an Object

Use with Student Edition pages 16–17.

Complete your own word web about a living thing you have observed in nature. Include sensory details.

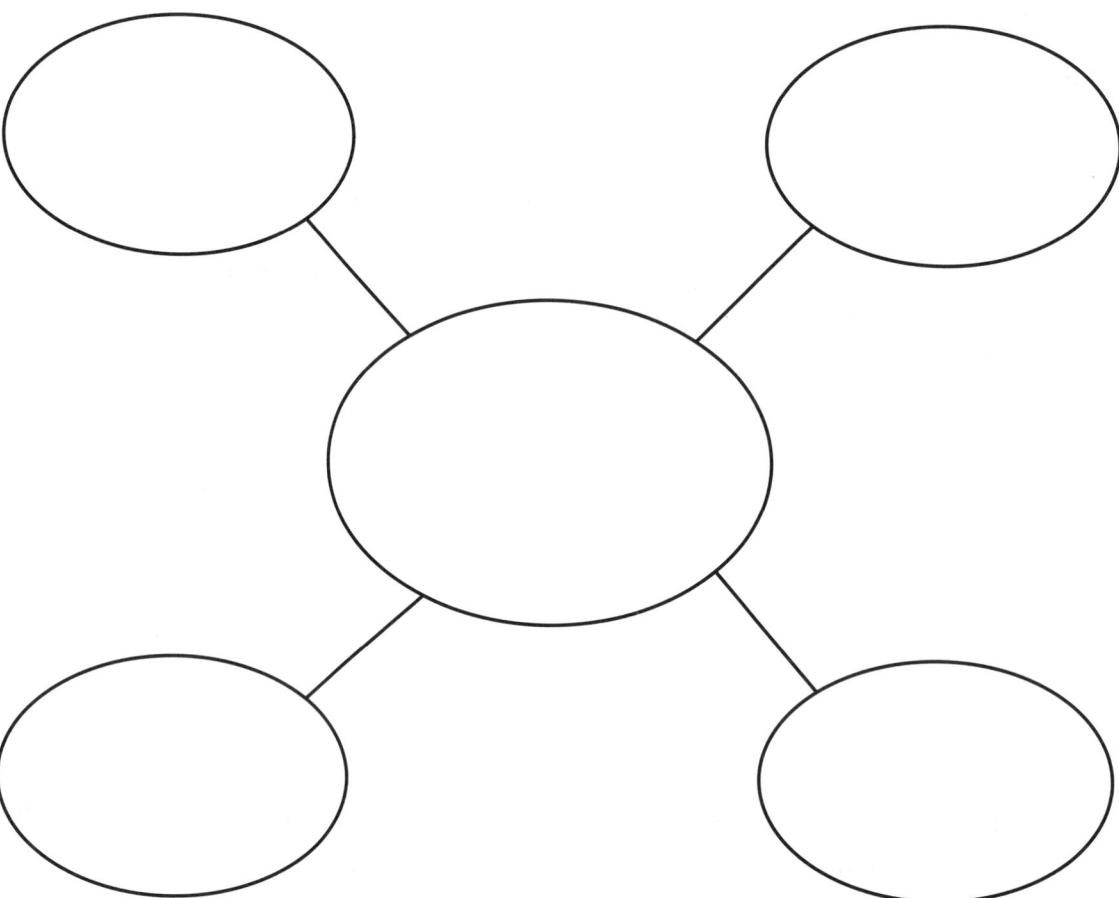

Have your partner complete (✓) the Peer Review Checklist. Use this feedback to help you edit your final draft.

Peer Review Checklist
- ☐ Does the paragraph describe a living thing?
- ☐ Do details appeal to a reader's senses?
- ☐ Does the writer present details in an order that makes sense?
- ☐ Are new vocabulary words used accurately?
- ☐ Are adjectives used correctly after indefinite pronouns?
- ☐ Could changes be made to improve the paragraph?

Name _____ Date _____

 **How does the natural world affect us?**

Reading 2: "Ecosystems: The Systems of Nature"

Vocabulary **Key Words** Use with Student Edition page 19.

Write each Key Word in the word box next to its definition.

| nonliving | nutrients | organism | photosynthesis | reproduce | species |

Example: __nonliving__: not alive

1. _____: produce new individuals of the same kind

2. _____: a living thing

3. _____: vitamins and minerals that help an organism stay healthy

4. _____: a category of living things that can reproduce with each other

5. _____: the process by which plants make food from water, light, and carbon dioxide

Use the Key Words in the word box to complete the sentences.

6. An ecosystem includes plants, animals, and _____ things such as sand and rocks.

7. An _____ can be as small as a single cell or as large as a whale.

8. Only members of the same _____ are able to _____ with each other.

9. Plants make their own food by _____.

10. Plants get _____ from the soil.

Unit 1 • Reading 2

Vocabulary **Academic Words** *Use with Student Edition page 20.*

Read the paragraph below. Pay attention to the underlined Academic Words.

> Giant pandas are similar to other bears, but pandas eat a special plant. Pandas consume bamboo. A giant panda must eat 20–30 pounds of bamboo each day to survive. Pandas are shy animals, so it's hard to study how they interact with each other in the wild. Because there are not many pandas in the world, their natural environment should be protected.

Match each word with its definition.

__b__ environment a. have an effect on each other

____ 1. survive b. the world of land, sea, and air that we live in

____ 2. consume c. continue to live

____ 3. interact d. eat or use something

Use the Academic Words from the exercise above to complete the sentences.

4. Carnivores only _____ other animals.

5. Dogs and cats sometimes _____ with one another.

6. In an extremely cold _____, animals have to work hard just to _____.

Complete the sentences with your own ideas.

Example: In the very dry environment of the desert, _cactus are able to grow_.

7. Farmers interact with animals such as _____.

8. A spider can consume _____.

9. A polar bear would struggle to survive in the _____.

10 Unit 1 • Reading 2

Name _____ Date _____

Word Study — Decoding Strategies: Digraphs

Use with Student Edition page 21.

> **REMEMBER** A digraph is a pair of letters that are pronounced together to make one sound, for example *ea* in the word *eat*. The *ea* sounds like *ee*.

Here are some more examples of diagraphs.

ue	au	aw	ee	ay	ai	oo	oa
ch	ff	gh	gn	kn	ll	mb	ng
nk	ph	qu	sh	ss	th	wh	wr

Read the passage below. Find each digraph, sound it out, and then underline it.

    China is facing serious environmental challenges. China is trying to feed 20 percent of the world's population on 7 percent of the world's fertile land. One third of the world uses water from China's rivers. But rapid industrialization and climate changes have led to polluted air and rivers, as well as drought. There is an ongoing struggle to fix these problems.

    The South-North Water Diversion plan is one possible solution. Once completed, it will be the world's largest water project. It will transfer water from the Yangtze basin in the south of China and move it up all the way up to the very dry northern China. The north part of China includes cities such as Beijing and Tianjin. This project involves hundreds of miles of canals. It will have to move water uphill, under the Yellow River, and through icy mountains.

    This project will cost billions of dollars. Large areas will need to be flooded to make way for reservoirs. Over 300,000 people will have to move and be resettled.

    Some critics believe that this project is a waste of money, because water pipes often leak and 40 percent of water could be lost. This water project could also increase water pollution. But the government in China is determined to move forward with this project.

Unit 1 • Reading 2

Reading Strategy | Preview for Main Idea and Details

Use with Student Edition page 21.

REMEMBER Before you read an article, preview it by asking yourself "What is this article about?" When you preview, think about what you already know about the topic. Next, look at the title, headings, pictures, photographs, charts, graphs, or maps. Think about your purpose for reading the text.

Preview the article. Then answer the questions that follow.

The Ecosystem of Death Valley
Life in an Extreme Environment

Death Valley is red hot. Its temperature has reached a blazing 134 degrees Fahrenheit! Location and low altitude make Death Valley one of the hottest and driest places on the planet.

Creatures survive in the desert by adapting. Many are nocturnal. Some have other tricks. The fringe-toed lizard's feet let it run across the sand at 10 miles per hour!

Many desert plants, such as the cactus, can survive for long stretches of time without any water.

1. Circle the first thing you looked at when you previewed this article.

2. What other parts of the article did you pay attention to as you previewed? Write an X next to each part that helped you to preview.

3. What do you think is the main idea of the article?

   _____

4. What details from the article helped you to answer the third question?

   _____

5. Imagine you're going to read the article on this page. Set a purpose for reading it.

   _____

Name _____ Date _____

Comprehension Use with Student Edition page 28.

Choose the *best* answer for each item. Circle the letter of the correct answer.

1. Cats and dogs cannot have offspring because they are different _____.

    a. bacteria　　　　**b.** species　　　　**c.** nonliving things

2. A desert and a lake are very different _____.

    a. populations　　**b.** organisms　　　**c.** habitats

3. All the black bears in one forest are _____.

    a. an ecosystem　　**b.** a population　　**c.** fungi

4. Herbivores, carnivores, and omnivores are the three types of _____.

    a. consumers　　　**b.** producers　　　**c.** decomposers

5. A food chain begins with producers and ends with _____.

    a. herbivores　　　**b.** consumers　　　**c.** decomposers

Extension Use with Student Edition page 29.

Write the names of five animals you like in the chart. Then research what kind of food each animal eats in the natural world. In the chart, write whether each animal is an herbivore, carnivore, or omnivore.

Animal	Type
frog	carnivore

Unit 1 • Reading 2

Grammar: Subject-Verb Agreement: Non-Count and Irregular-Plural Nouns
Use with Student Edition page 30.

REMEMBER In the simple present, the subject and the verb must agree in number. Add -s or -es to verbs if the subject is a singular noun or a singular subject pronoun, such as *he*, *she*, and *it*. Don't add -s or -es to verbs if the subject is a plural noun.

Look at the following sentences. If the sentence is correct, write *correct* on the line next to it. If it is incorrect, rewrite the sentence using the correct form of the verb.

Example: A horse eat grass. <u>A horse eats grass.</u>

1. The class take care of a young puppy. _____
2. Clouds are part of the water cycle. _____
3. The kids live near the ocean. _____
4. Vapor rise into the air. _____

REMEMBER A non-count noun is a noun that cannot be counted. When the subject of a sentence in the simple present is a non-count noun, use a singular verb (add -s or -es). If the verb is *be*, use *is*. When irregular plural nouns are the subject of a sentence in the simple present, they always take a plural verb (do not add -s or -es).

Complete the table with words from the box.

~~cheese~~ ~~sandwich~~ teeth mice ice wind children sheep tea sugar

Count Nouns	Non-count Nouns
sandwich	cheese

Name _____ Date _____

Grammar — Comparison Structures *Use with Student Edition page 31.*

> **REMEMBER** Use a comparison structure such as *as ____ as* with an adverb or adjective; use *so ____ that* with an adverb; and use *similarly* at the beginning of a sentence to compare one thing to another.

Complete the sentences with *as _____ as*, *so _____ that*, or *similarly*.

Example: A tree can grow __as__ tall __as__ a building.

1. Herbivores eat only plants. _____, carnivores eat only meat.

2. The lion grew _____ hungry _____ it began looking for food.

3. A gazelle is not _____ fast _____ a cheetah, but it can run for longer periods of time.

Read each pair of sentences. Choose a comparison structure to form one or two new sentences. Use *as _____ as*, *so _____ that*, or *similarly*.

Example: The man was tired. ⟶ He fell asleep in the middle of the day.

The man was so tired that he fell asleep in the middle of the day.

4. Some monarch butterflies migrate each year from Canada to Mexico. ⟶ Some whales swim across several oceans in one year.

_____
_____
_____

5. The blue whale can grow to be large. ⟶ It can be the same size as an office building.

_____
_____
_____

Unit 1 • Reading 2

Writing: Write a Description of a Place

Use with Student Edition pages 32–33.

Complete your own chart about a place you enjoy. Describe it in spatial order.

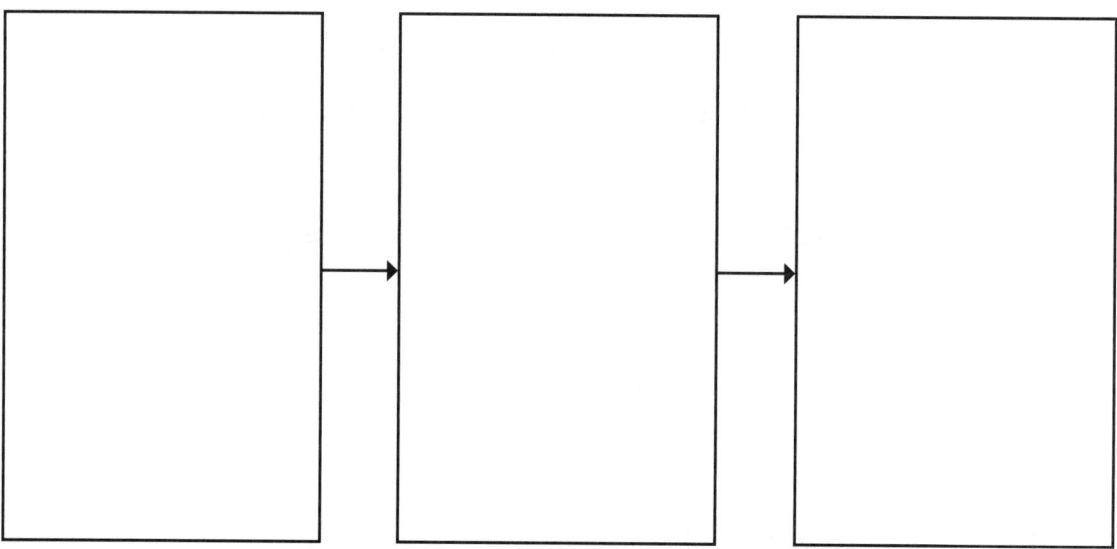

Have your partner complete (✓) the Peer Review Checklist. Use this feedback to help you edit your final draft.

Peer Review Checklist

- ☐ Does the paragraph describe a place close to nature?
- ☐ Is this place described with specificity and detail?
- ☐ Are details arranged using spatial order?
- ☐ Is the writing voice clear and lively?
- ☐ Do subjects and verbs agree in number?
- ☐ Are comparison structures used correctly?
- ☐ Could any changes be made to improve the paragraph?

Name _____   Date _____

How does the natural world affect us?

Reading 3: "Ali, Child of the Desert" / "Desert Women"

Vocabulary   **Literary Words** *Use with Student Edition page 35.*

> **REMEMBER** **Figurative language** is writing that is not meant to be read as fact. For instance, **personification** gives human qualities to nonliving things. **Setting** is the time and place of a story's action.

Write whether the sentences are an example of personification or setting.

Example: ____setting____ The sky was full of dark rain clouds.

1. _____ The tree's branches grabbed at Irving.

2. _____ The engine hummed.

3. _____ Alex's house was cozy and warm.

4. _____ The boat called her to come and sail away.

5. _____ The desert was empty of people.

In the following passage, underline examples of personification. Circle words that provide clues to the setting.

> It was the middle of winter. My grandmother's house stood on a hill. The house was old and poorly heated. The wind howled through the windows. The floorboards moaned as we walked on them.

Unit 1 • Reading 3

Vocabulary — Academic Words Use with Student Edition page 36.

Read the paragraph below. Pay attention to the underlined Academic Words.

> I read a book about the Sahara desert. I <u>concluded</u> that it would be an interesting place to visit. However, I would have to <u>adapt</u> to the extreme heat during the day. I would need to <u>rely</u> on a guide to lead the way through the desert. I would need a <u>capable</u> guide who knew the best route through the desert.

Write the Academic Words from the paragraph above next to their correct definitions.

Example: ____rely____ : trust someone or something

1. _____ : able to do something
2. _____ : made a decision based on evidence
3. _____ : change something so that it is suitable for a new situation

Use the Academic Words from the exercise above to complete the sentences.

4. The animals were able to _____ to changes in their environment.
5. She didn't ask for help, so we _____ that she was capable of doing it on her own.
6. The travelers were in the desert and had to _____ on watering holes to keep their camels refreshed.

Complete the sentences with your own ideas.

Example: I have recently had to adapt to ____moving to a new town____.

7. Among my friends, I know I can always rely on _____.
8. Most people don't know I'm capable of _____.

Name _____ Date _____

Word Study — Compound Nouns *Use with Student Edition page 37.*

REMEMBER A compound noun is made up of two or more words. Compound nouns can be written as one word, as in *sunglasses*. They can be written as two separate words, as in *rock music*. They can be written with a hyphen, as in *brother-in-law*. Check the compound noun in a dictionary if you are not sure how to spell it.

Read the compound nouns in the box. Then write the compound nouns in the correct column in the chart.

~~airport~~	help desk	know-it-all	aircraft	life span
self-esteem	voice mail	earring	hanger-on	waiting room
fingerprint	earthquake	ground water	hand-me-down	trade-off

One Word	Hyphenated Words	Two Words
airport	5.	10.
1.	6.	11.
2.	7.	12.
3.	8.	13.
4.	9.	14.

Create compound nouns by combining words. Check in a dictionary to see if the compound noun is written as one word, separate words, or a hyphenated word.

| paper | print | brush | stamp | cake | paint | portrait |
| ~~book~~ | pan | self | foot | ~~text~~ | postage | towel |

Example: text + book = textbook

15. _____ 18. _____

16. _____ 19. _____

17. _____ 20. _____

Reading Strategy — Visualize

Use with Student Edition page 37.

> **REMEMBER** As you read, try to visualize or picture what is being described in the text.

Read the passages below and underline the details that help you visualize the text. Next, draw the scene in the spaces provided.

1. Alice carried eight books up the library steps. On the tenth step, she tripped on her long skirt and all the books flew out of her arms. The books tumbled down the library steps.

2. The lake lies still
   And the trees are
   Heavy with fruit
   Against a pale, clear sky.

Read the passages below and picture the scenes in your head. Underline the details that help you visualize the scenes.

3. Ali rode at the rear of the herd. The sun blazed down on him. It seemed to Ali that he had been sitting atop his camel for weeks. But he had not complained about the heat, his thirst, or his sore legs.

4. The bookshelves were filled with row after row of old books. Beatrice could see dust hanging in the still air. She bent down and opened the book.

5. Nadya held out her hand, catching the rain. Her bare feet moved through the muddy grass.

Unit 1 • Reading 3

Comprehension   Use with Student Edition page 46.

Choose the *best* answer for each item. Circle the letter of the correct answer.

1. Ali gets lost in _____.

   a. an oasis   b. a sandstorm   c. the market

2. In the desert, Ali meets a Berber and his _____.

   a. assistant   b. son   c. grandson

3. Abdul reveals that he was once a _____.

   a. herdsman   b. warrior   c. bandit

4. To help his father find him, Ali _____.

   a. fires a musket   b. leaves with Abdul c. leaves a trail of bread

5. The poem "Desert Women" compares these women to _____.

   a. the desert   b. cactus   c. heat and cold

Response to Literature   Use with Student Edition page 47.

Pretend that you are Ali. On the lines below, describe what it's like to be in a sandstorm.

_____
_____
_____
_____
_____
_____
_____
_____

Unit 1 • Reading 3

Grammar Simple Sentences: Consistent Forms, Parallel **Structure** Use with Student Edition page 48.

> **REMEMBER** Be sure to be consistent with verb forms. For example, if you begin using simple past verbs, continue using simple past verbs. Be sure to use parallel structure. Parallel structure is using the same pattern of words to tell about similar things. For example, word order should be similar. Also, you should not mix -ed and -ing adjectives, infinitives and gerunds, or phrases and clauses.

Complete each sentence with the correct form of the verb in parentheses.

Example: I met Fran at the concert last night. We (get) __got__ something to eat afterward.

1. Alfonso wrote me a long letter. I finally (read) _____ it yesterday.

2. My brother works for a company downtown. He (start) _____ work very early.

3. I never get up early on Saturdays. I always (sleep) _____ late.

4. Sheila was in Santiago last week. She (bring) _____ me back a beautiful necklace.

Rewrite each sentence, correcting the error in parallel structure.

Example: I enjoy skiing, snowboarding, and to swim.

  I enjoy skiing, snowboarding, and swimming.

5. The movie we saw was long, silly, and bored.
   _____

6. My little brother, Sam, and Joe, my older brother, can both sing.
   _____

7. Susan appeared to be angry, upset, and to be sad about her grades.
   _____

8. He is smart, funny, and is nice.
   _____

Name _____ Date _____

Grammar — Adjectival Phrases: Adjective Order

Use with Student Edition page 49.

> **REMEMBER** Adjectives are words that describe people, places, and things. When you use more than one adjective before a noun, you must put the adjectives in this order: opinion, size, color, material.

Complete the lists with words from the box.

| cloth | black | plastic | tiny | beautiful |
| little | cool | sugar | pink | large |

Opinion	Size	Color	Material
ugly	big	purple	wood
interesting		orange	

Complete the sentences with the adjectives in parentheses. Write the adjectives in the correct order.

Example: (black, cool) She's wearing a __cool__ __black__ jacket.

1. (cloth, little) Look at this _____ _____ notebook.

2. That's an (interesting, orange) _____ _____ flower.

3. He bought a (beautiful, silk, yellow) _____ _____ _____ shirt.

4. It's a (chocolate, white, delicious) _____ _____ _____ dessert.

5. They live in a (brick, huge, red) _____ _____ _____ house.

Unit 1 • Reading 3

Writing — Write a Description of a Person

Use with Student Edition pages 50–51.

Complete your own T-chart about someone you know well. Describe physical and character traits.

Physical traits	Character traits

Have your partner complete (✓) the Peer Review Checklist. Use this feedback to help you edit your final draft.

Peer Review Checklist
- ☐ Does the paragraph describe someone the writer knows?
- ☐ Does it describe both physical traits and character traits?
- ☐ Does the writer choose precise words and details?
- ☐ Are verb forms consistent in parallel structures?
- ☐ Are adjectives in adjectival phrases in the correct order?
- ☐ Could any changes be made to improve the paragraph?

Name _____ Date _____

Writing Workshop   *Use with Student Edition pages 56–59.*

Organize your ideas in the graphic organizer below.

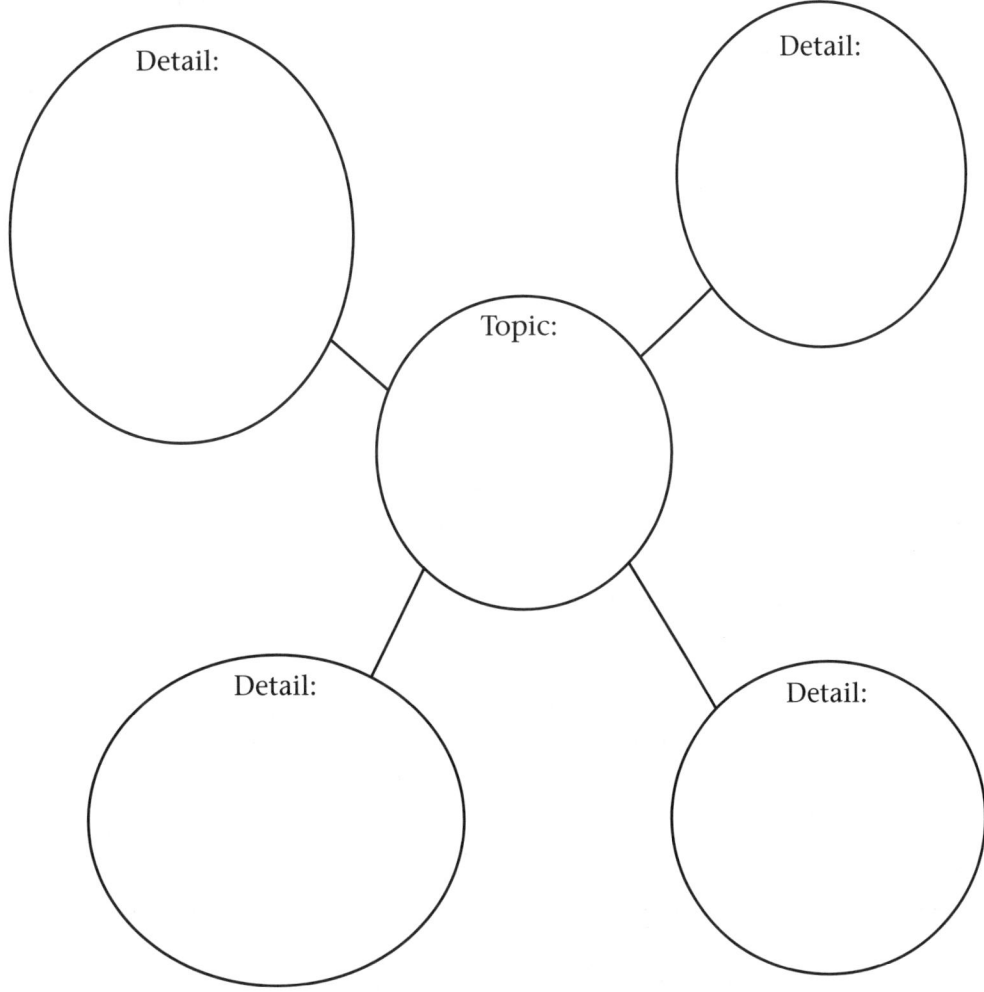

Have your partner complete (✓) the Peer Review Checklist. Use this feedback to help you edit your final draft.

Peer Review Checklist

☐ Does the essay sustain my interest?
☐ Does it have an introduction and a conclusion?
☐ Do the words and details appeal to my senses?
☐ Do the sentences vary in length and pattern?
☐ Do subjects and verbs agree in number?
☐ Could changes be made to improve the essay?

Unit 1 • Writing Workshop

Learning Log *Use after completing Student Edition page 60.*

Underline the vocabulary items you know and can use well. Review and practice any you haven't underlined. Underline them when you know them well.

Literary Words	Key Words	Academic Words	
imagery sensory details figurative language personification setting	nonliving nutrients organism photosynthesis reproduce species	cultural cycle migration traditional consume environment	interact survive adapt capable concluded rely

Put a check by the skills you can perform well. Review and practice any you haven't checked off. Check them off when you can perform them well.

Skills	I can . . .
Word Study	☐ recognize and use the prefixes *in-*, *re-*, *over-*, and *un-*. ☐ decode digraphs. ☐ recognize and use compound nouns.
Reading Strategies	☐ predict. ☐ preview for main idea and details. ☐ visualize.
Grammar	☐ use adjectives after indefinite pronouns. ☐ use prenominal and postnominal adjectives. ☐ use correct subject/verb agreement with non-count and irregular-plural nouns. ☐ use comparison structures correctly. ☐ use consistent forms and parallel structures in simple sentences. ☐ use adjectives in the correct order in adjectival phrases.
Writing	☐ write a description of an object. ☐ write a description of a place. ☐ write a description of a person. ☐ write descriptive paragraphs and essays.

Name _____ Date _____

Test Preparation

Test 1

DIRECTIONS
Read this selection. Then answer the questions that follow it.

Mr. Yee's class is studying hurricanes. Gina finds this chart in a book from the library. Mr. Yee wants her to share the information with the class. Jason tells the class that he had traveled to Florida, U.S.A., when Hurricane Charley hit. He and his family were caught in the storm.

Six Most Damaging Hurricanes to Hit the United States (1985–2010)

Name	Year	Location	Hurricane Wind Scale	Wind Speed (miles per hour)
1. Katrina	2007	Louisiana, Mississippi	Category 4	140
2. Andrew	1992	Florida, Louisiana	Category 5	165
3. Charley	2004	Florida	Category 4	145
4. Ivan	2004	Alabama, Florida	Category 3	108
5. Frances	2004	Florida	Category 2	94
6. Hugo	1989	South Carolina	Category 4	140

1 Where was the most damaging storm?
   A Alabama
   B Florida
   C Mississippi
   D South Carolina

2 From the passage, what can you infer about where Jason is *least* likely to live?
   A Alabama
   B Florida
   C Louisiana
   D South Carolina

Test 2

DIRECTIONS
Read this selection. Then answer the questions that follow it.

Death Valley, California, U.S.A.

California's Death Valley is a land of extremes. In fact, it is one of the driest, hottest, and lowest places on the face of the earth. It is an extremely dry land. Its average annual rainfall is less than 2 inches. That means that there are some years with less than 2 inches of rain! It is also extremely hot. In 1913, the thermometer recorded a temperature of 134 degrees Fahrenheit, the second-highest temperature ever recorded on Earth. Summer temperatures routinely climb above 120 degrees Fahrenheit. The valley is also extremely low. Almost 550 square miles of the valley lie below sea level. The lowest point in the western hemisphere is located here. With such extremes, it is doubtful that Death Valley attracts many tourists.

Death Valley Extremes		
Extremely Hot	Extremely Dry	Extremely Low
134 degrees	less than 2 inches of rainfall	550 square miles below sea level
Other Extremes in the United States		
Extremely Cold	Extremely Wet	Extremely High
–79.8 degrees Prospect Creek Camp Endicott Mountains, Alaska	67 inches of rainfall annually Mobile, Alabama	20,320 feet above sea level Mt. McKinley, Alaska

1 Which of these sentences from "Death Valley" is an opinion?
  A *That means that there are some years with less than 2 inches of rain!*
  B *The valley is also extremely low.*
  C *With such extremes, it is doubtful that Death Valley attracts many tourists.*
  D *The lowest point in the western hemisphere is located here.*

2 What is the purpose of the chart?
  A To give more information about the extreme conditions in Death Valley
  B To warn readers that visiting Death Valley is dangerous
  C To compare and contrast Death Valley with other extreme places
  D To inform readers about other places that are extremely dry, low, and hot

3 What does the word *annual* mean?
  A yearly
  B monthly
  C daily
  D weekly

4 The tone of the article is —
  A factual
  B humorous
  C excited
  D angry

Name _____ Date _____

Test 3

DIRECTIONS
Read this selection. Then answer the questions that follow it.

Plants

1   Plants make food by <u>photosynthesis</u>. In Greek, *photo* means "light." *Synthesis* means "make." Plants use light to make food. The light usually comes from the sun.

2   Plants get energy from sunlight. They use the energy to change water and carbon dioxide (CAR-buhn-deye-OX-eyed) into sugar and oxygen (OX-uh-jin). The sugar is the plant's food. The oxygen goes out into the air. People and other animals need the oxygen to breathe.

3   Many plants use seeds to make new plants. Inside a seed is a new plant and stored food. The new plant does not grow until it gets the right amount of water, heat, and light.

4   When seeds land on the ground, they can begin a new cycle of plant life. Rain falls, and the seeds begin to grow. Roots break out of the seeds and grow down into the ground. Leaves and the stem grow up above the ground toward the sunlight. The plants produce flowers. Insects and other animals pollinate the flowers. A fruit forms with new seeds inside it. These new seeds land on the ground. These repeated events make up the plant life cycle.

5   Plants are important. You can look around your school and home to find different ways that people use plants. For example, people eat fruit, grains, and vegetables. People also build things with different kinds of wood. People wear clothes made from cotton plants. Even hair shampoo contains plant products.

1 Look at this diagram of the plant life cycle.

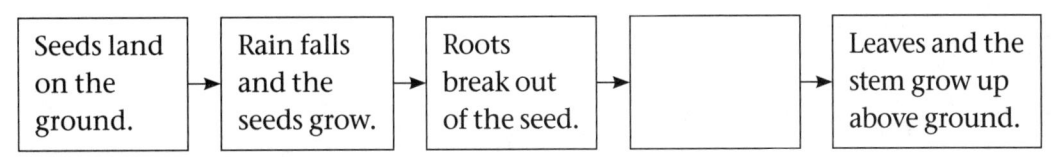

| Seeds land on the ground. | → | Rain falls and the seeds grow. | → | Roots break out of the seed. | → | | → | Leaves and the stem grow up above ground. |

Which of these belongs in the empty box?

A The plant produces flowers.
B Insects pollinate the flowers.
C A fruit forms with new seeds.
D Roots grow down into the ground.

2 Paragraph 4 is mainly about —
  A uses of plants
  B plant life cycle
  C parts of a plant
  D plants and photosynthesis

3 In paragraph 1, what does the word *photosynthesis* mean?
  A Light usually comes from the sun
  B Plants make food
  C Use light to make food
  D Plants need light

4 According to the article, where might fruits, grains, and vegetables be found?
  A In homes and schools
  B In the rainforest
  C In businesses
  D At the supermarket

5 How is "Plants" organized?
  A It moves from an introduction to a detailed description of the plant life cycle, to a detailed description of the uses of plants.
  B It moves from a description of how plants make food, to a detailed description of the life cycle, to a general description of the uses of plants.
  C It moves from a list of questions about plants to detailed answers.
  D It moves from a detailed description of how plants make food to a general description of the plant life cycle.

Name _____ Date _____

Visual Literacy: Smithsonian American Art Museum
Use with Student Edition pages 62–63.

Learning to Look

Look at *Among the Sierra Nevada, California* by Albert Bierstadt on page 76 in your textbook. Write four words to describe this painting. State facts, not opinions.

Example: _____mountains_____

1. _____ 3. _____
2. _____ 4. _____

Interpretation

Look at *Among the Sierra Nevada, California* again. Imagine that you are walking through this landscape. Then answer the questions.

1. What do you see?

_____

_____

_____

2. What do you hear?

_____

_____

_____

3. How do you feel about being here?

_____

_____

_____

5W&H

Imagine that you are with Albert Bierstadt in his studio at the time he is painting this work. What would you ask him? Complete the questions below.

Example: *What does the title of the painting mean?*

1. Who
2. What
3. Where
4. When
5. Why
6. How

Name _____ Date _____

UNIT 2: Where can a journey take you?

Reading 1: from *Tales from the Odyssey*

Vocabulary

Literary Words *Use with Student Edition page 67.*

> **REMEMBER** A **character** is a person who takes part in the action of a story. A **plot** is a sequence of connected events in a story. A story's **point of view** is the perspective from which the story is told. In the **first-person point of view**, a narrator tells his or her own story. In the **third-person point of view**, a narrator tells someone else's story.

Match each term in Column A to its meaning in Column B.

Column A	Column B
Example: plot	a person's way of seeing a situation
1. character	a narrator tells someone else's story
2. point of view	a narrator tells his or her own story
3. first-person point of view	a story's sequence of events
4. third-person point of view	a person who takes part in the action of a story

Read the story. Draw a circle around the name of each character. Underline each event in the plot. Then answer the question below.

Grand Journey

Pam really wanted to visit the Grand Canyon in Arizona, U.S.A. to see it with her own eyes. She asked her mom and dad about it several times. Finally, they said yes. Pam studied maps and planned the route. One evening, her mom said, "If we leave tomorrow, we'll be there by Monday."

The next day, the family left on their trip. First, the car had a flat tire. Then they got lost. Next, her dad lost his wallet. Finally, they reached the Grand Canyon. It was worth the trip!

---

5. What point of view is the story written in? _____

Unit 2 • Reading 1

Vocabulary   **Academic Words** *Use with Student Edition page 68.*

Read the paragraph below. Pay attention to the underlined Academic Words.

> Each year, cities along the coast <u>attribute</u> many accidents and injuries to hurricanes. Before a major hurricane, people are advised to <u>abandon</u> their homes and get to safety. They are advised to <u>react</u> quickly in order to ease crowding on the roads. They are warned to stay away until the storm <u>finally</u> passes. Following these tips can help people stay safe.

Match each word with its definition.

Example: __d__ attribute

_____ 1. finally   **a.** behave in a certain way because of what someone has done or said to you

_____ 2. abandon   **b.** after a long time

_____ 3. react   **c.** leave someone or something that you are responsible for

                                    d. blame something on another person or event

Use the Academic Words from the exercise above to complete the sentences.

4. When the fire alarm went off at midnight, people in the building had to _____ quickly.

5. They needed to wake up, gather their families, and _____ their apartments.

6. It took a long time for the firefighters to put out the fire, but _____, at 4:00 a.m., it was extinguished.

7. Officials _____ the fire to an accident from a lower floor where a burning candle was left unattended.

Name _____ Date _____

Word Study — Roots *vict, laps, mem, mand*

Use with Student Edition page 69.

> **REMEMBER** Roots are the base part of a word. The root **vict** means "conquer" as in *victor*. The root **laps** means "slip" as in *lapse*. The root **mem** means "mind" as in *remember*. The root **mand** means "order" as in *mandate*.

Look at the chart below. List the root in each word. Write the meaning of the root and the meaning of the word on the chart. Use a dictionary if needed.

Word	Root	Root Meaning	Word Meaning
memorize	mem	mind	to commit to memory
1. commander			
2. victim			
3. relapse			

Circle the root in each word below. Then write the definition next to the word. Use a dictionary if needed.

Example: de(mand) *a firm and insistent request*

4. memorable _____

5. elapse _____

6. mandatory _____

7. victorious _____

8. memorial _____

9. lapse _____

10. eviction _____

Reading Strategy: Identify Problems and Solutions

Use with Student Edition page 69.

REMEMBER To identify a **problem** and a **solution** in a story, ask, "What is the character's problem?" "What does the character do to solve his or her problem?" "How is the problem solved at the end of the story?"

Read the story. Then answer the questions that follow.

A Big Favor

Marta was worried. Her teacher had asked her to carry a computer to the library. First, Marta tried to carry it all by herself. It was too heavy, and she had to put it down on a desk. Then she asked a friend to help her. However, the friend was rushing to music class and could not help her. Finally, Marta explained to her teacher that the computer was too heavy. Then the teacher smiled and helped her carry the computer to the library. The teacher thanked Marta very much for her help.

1. Identify the problem in the story. _____
2. Identify the solution in the story. _____

Read the story and complete the chart.

The Queen's Contest

The queen announced a contest. She promised to give a castle to any person who could figure out her secret name and write a song about it. Alanna figured out the queen's secret name, but she did not know how to write a song. Jean wrote wonderful songs, but she did not know the queen's secret name. So the two girls decided to work together. Alanna told Jean the queen's secret name. Jean wrote a lovely song about the queen's name. The girls presented the song to the queen. The queen was delighted and gave the girls a castle.

Character	Character's Problem	How does the character solve the problem?
3. Alanna		
4. Jean		

5. How the problem was solved:

Name _____ Date _____

Comprehension   Use with Student Edition page 74.

Choose the best answer for each item. Circle the letter of the correct answer.

1. The main character in the story is _____.

   a. Poseidon   b. Odysseus   c. Athena

2. The gods were angry because the Greeks _____.

   a. offended Athena   b. used weak ships   c. feared the waves

3. The Greeks survived the storm because _____.

   a. the sun came out   b. the goddess helped them   c. they rowed to shore

4. Odysseus sailed his fleet to the island to _____.

   a. repair their ship   b. find food and drink   c. meet the island people

5. Odysseus's men did not answer him because they had _____.

   a. eaten magic flowers   b. drunk a magic potion   c. died of hunger

Response to Literature   Use with Student Edition page 75.

Find a scene in the story that you can see clearly in your mind. Draw a picture that shows the scene.

Unit 2 • Reading 1

Grammar — Simple Past: Regular and Irregular Verbs

Use with Student Edition page 76.

> **REMEMBER** The **simple past** of regular verbs is formed by adding *-d* or *-ed* to the base form of the verb. If the verb ends in a consonant and *y*, change the *y* to an *i* and add *-ed*. The simple past of irregular verbs is formed differently and must be memorized. For example, the simple past of *be* is *was* and *were*. The negative is *was not* (the contraction is *wasn't*) and *were not* (the contraction is *weren't*). Begin questions with *was* or *were*.

Complete the chart with the simple past form of each verb.

Base Form	Simple Past: Regular	Base Form	Simple Past: Irregular
1. ask		6. do	
2. smile		7. get	
3. cry		8. grow	
4. hope		9. have	
5. answer		10. go	

Rewrite the sentences in the simple past using the words in parentheses.

Example: The captain (try) a new route. (last night)
The captain tried a new route last night.

11. They (reach) their destination. (on Monday)

_____

12. They (be) in Japan. (last weekend)

_____

13. The captain (tell) them his new plan. (this morning)

_____

14. The sailor (save) a seashell from each place they went. (last year)

_____

Name _____ Date _____

Grammar — Simple Sentences: Pronouns and Modifiers

Use with Student Edition page 77.

> **REMEMBER** A **simple sentence** has a noun and a predicate, which is a word or phrase that contains a verb and tells more about the noun. All nouns and pronouns must agree in number (singular or plural) and in gender (masculine, for example, *he*; feminine, for example, *she*; or neutral, for example, *it*). Pronouns must correctly refer to their antecedents, or the noun that comes before them. An adjective can go before the noun it modifies, after a linking verb, or before an indefinite pronoun.

Circle all the antecedents in each sentence. Then underline the pronouns that refer to them.

Example: (Maya) drew (a picture) of <u>herself</u>. I thought <u>it</u> was very good.

1. The students were noisy. Many people were staring at them.
2. The class is too small. It is going to be canceled.
3. Our house is large. It has three floors and six bedrooms.
4. Senad gave me his phone number. I gave him mine, too.

Rewrite each sentence, placing the adjective(s) in the correct place.

Example: We ate a meal delicious last night. *We ate a delicious meal last night.*

5. Did you learn interesting anything in school today?

   _____

6. He angry became with me.

   _____

7. The dancer talented gave a performance great.

   _____

8. The hungry cats were.

   _____

Unit 2 • Reading 1

Writing — **Write a Story from a Different Point of View**

Use with Student Edition pages 78–79.

Complete your own T-chart comparing and contrasting two points of view from a familiar story. One of the two narrators should be a character in the story.

Have your partner complete (✓) the Peer Review Checklist. Use this feedback to help you edit your final draft.

Peer Review Checklist
- ☐ Does the writer retell a familiar story?
- ☐ Is the story retold from a character's point of view?
- ☐ Does the writing voice fit the story's narrator?
- ☐ Are pronouns used correctly?
- ☐ Is the simple past used correctly for regular and irregular verbs?
- ☐ Could changes be made to improve the story?

Name _____ Date _____

UNIT 2: Where can a journey take you?

Reading 2: "Migrating Caribou" / "Magnets in Animals"

Vocabulary — Key Words *Use with Student Edition page 81.*

Write each word in the box next to its definition.

| biologists | herd | landscape | magnetic | range | starvation |

Example: ___range___ : the limits or distance of a place

1. _____ : having the power of a magnet

2. _____ : scientists who study living things

3. _____ : suffering or death caused by not having enough to eat

4. _____ : a view across an area of land

5. _____ : a group of a particular type of animal that lives together

Use the words in the box at the top of the page to complete the sentences.

6. The _____ of the black bear extends into central Mexico.

7. Several _____ studied the eating and sleeping habits of the caribou.

8. Some animals that live in harsh conditions die of _____.

9. A compass uses Earth's _____ field to point toward the North Pole.

10. The Arctic _____ has no trees.

11. The largest _____ of antelope lives in southern Africa and numbers in the millions.

Unit 2 • Reading 2   41

Vocabulary — Academic Words *Use with Student Edition page 82.*

Read the paragraph below. Pay attention to the underlined Academic Words.

> In the spring and summer, many birds live in <u>areas</u> in the north. As cold weather <u>approaches</u>, finding food starts to become difficult. At this time, many birds <u>migrate</u> to warmer climates. Some birds travel an <u>approximate</u> distance of a thousand miles south over the ocean without stopping.

Match each word with its definition.

Example: __b__ approximate   **a.** move from one place to another

_____ 1. approaches   **b.** nearly

_____ 2. area   **c.** moves closer

_____ 3. migrate   **d.** a section of land

Use the Academic Words from the exercise above to complete the sentences.

4. Some birds _____ south in the winter.

5. A mother animal will often protect her babies from anyone who _____ them.

6. One-half cup of water a week is the _____ amount required for that plant.

7. The _____ containing forest covers two hundred acres.

Complete the sentences with your own ideas.

Example: The area of town I like best is ___the shopping district___.

8. A zookeeper carefully approaches a _____.

9. For my favorite recipe, I use approximately _____.

10. Many birds migrate from northern areas to _____.

Name _____ Date _____

Word Study   Words as Multiple Parts of Speech

Use with Student Edition page 83.

> **REMEMBER** A **noun** is a person, place, or thing. An **adjective** is a word that modifies (describes) a noun. Some words can be used as both nouns and adjectives. For example: I like *fall*. (noun). It was a crisp *fall* day. (adjective)

Look at the chart below. Identify the underlined word as a noun or an adjective. The first set is done for you.

1. An Italian won the gold medal. _____ noun _____
2. We like Italian food. _____
3. My friend is at summer camp. _____
4. Samantha loves winter. _____
5. The rich don't worry about money. _____
6. The chef made a rich dessert. _____
7. Math is easy for me. _____
8. We have science class now. _____
9. Look at the beautiful butterfly. _____
10. I bought a butterfly net. _____

Write a new sentence for each underlined word, changing it from an adjective to a noun.

Example: Summer days are my favorite of all. _____ I like summer. _____

11. We saw a Spanish movie over the weekend. _____
12. My uncle has garden gloves. _____
13. Many people like Idaho potatoes. _____
14. Luc drinks apple juice every morning. _____
15. The village bakery is very popular. _____

Unit 2 • Reading 2

Reading Strategy: Recognize Cause and Effect

Use with Student Edition page 83.

> **REMEMBER** A **cause** is a reason that something happens. What happens as the result of a cause is an **effect**. To find an effect, ask "What happened?" To find a cause, ask "Why did it happen?"

Read the following story. Then complete the exercise.

Li Wei and His Babysitting Job

Li Wei always babysat for George Robinson on Tuesday afternoons. Mrs. Robinson spent that time working at Dr. Lopez's office. One Tuesday afternoon, Li Wei's mother called him at school. "Come straight home after school today. I need your help planning a party for your grandma." Li Wei was so excited, he completely forgot about his babysitting job. Because of this, Mrs. Robinson had nobody to take care of George. She could not go to work. Because Mrs. Robinson did not go to work, Dr. Lopez could not help his patients. He closed his office early and canceled his appointments. His patients were not happy.

Use information from the article to complete the cause-and-effect chart below.

Cause	Effect
Cause: Li Wei's mother is planning a party for Li Wei's grandma.	**Effect:** Li Wei's mother tells him to come straight home after school.
1. Cause: Li Wei forgets to babysit for Mrs. Robinson.	**Effect:**
2. Cause: Mrs. Robinson cannot go to work at Dr. Lopez's office.	**Effect:**
3. Cause: Dr. Lopez closes his office early and cancels his appointments.	**Effect:**

Name _____ Date _____

Comprehension   Use with Student Edition page 88.

Choose the best answer for each item. Circle the letter of the correct answer.

1. Caribou move south to _____.

   a. create herds   b. find rivers   c. avoid starvation

2. South of the tree line _____.

   a. caribou find lichen to eat   b. no trees will grow   c. there are no biting flies

3. Caribou travel far north to have their babies because _____.

   a. the lichen is softer there   b. there are fewer predators there   c. the lakes are wider there

4. One animal that migrates more than 22,000 miles is the _____.

   a. Arctic tern   b. goldfish   c. caribou

5. Biologists think that some animals find their way by watching _____.

   a. other animals   b. the sun and stars   c. magnets

Extension   Use with Student Edition page 89.

Write the name of an animal that interests you. Then research details about the animal to complete the graphic organizer.

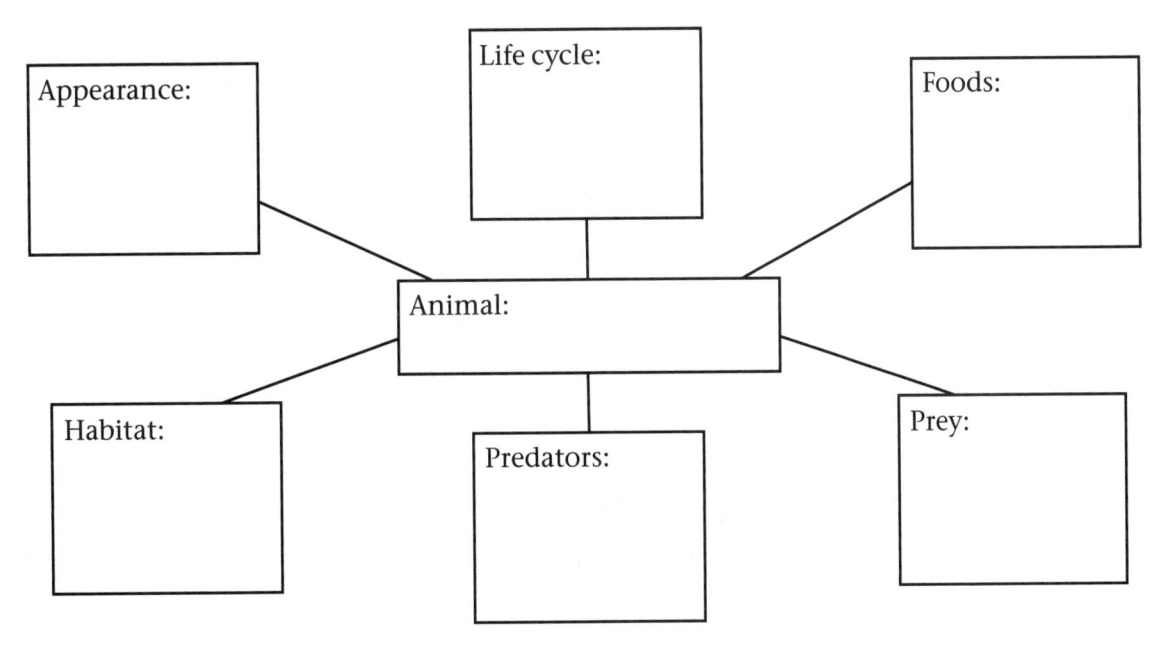

- Appearance:
- Life cycle:
- Foods:
- Animal:
- Habitat:
- Predators:
- Prey:

Unit 2 • Reading 2   45

Grammar — More on Parallel Structure Use with Student Edition page 90.

REMEMBER Parallel structure uses similar words and phrases to make your writing smoother and easier to understand. When your sentences and ideas aren't in parallel form, they can be hard to understand.

Correct the sentences below to be parallel.

Example: The caribou are good swimmers and steadily walking.
The caribou are good swimmers and steady walkers.

1. Along the way, the caribou encounter storms, predators, and experiencing dangers.

2. The caribou herd includes males, the females, and newborn calves.

3. Winter is cold, is dark, and food is hard to find.

4. Younger caribou travel in the back of the herd. The front of the herd is made up of the older caribou.

5. The caribou walked for miles, gave birth to their calves, and were eating a lot of plants.

Write P for Parallel or NP for Not Parallel after each sentence.

6. The caribou migrate to avoid predators and to find more food. _____

7. The sea turtle can be seen to swim to shore, laying eggs, and covering the eggs with sand. _____

8. Flying, swimming, and walking are three ways animals can migrate. _____

9. Monarch butterflies fly gracefully, swiftly, and efficient. _____

10. Predators include bears, the wolves, and mountain lions. _____

Name _____ Date _____

Grammar — Prepositions Use with Student Edition page 91.

> **REMEMBER** Prepositional phrases are made up of a preposition followed by a noun or noun phrase. **Prepositions** are used to show a relationship to another word in the phrase. They can show time, place, direction, or additional details. Some common prepositions include *about, across, after, around, at, before, behind, beside, between, by, for, in, into, of, on, over, to, under,* and *up*.

Choose the correct preposition from the word bank to complete each sentence.

| across | after | behind | on | over | under |

Example: __After__ the snow begins to melt, the caribou begin their migration.

1. The young calves travel _____ the older caribou.

2. Some birds fly _____ the ocean without stopping.

3. The caribou look for lichen _____ the crust of snow.

4. We saw a field of monarch butterflies sitting _____ milkweed plants.

5. After walking _____ many miles of frozen tundra, the caribou finally reach their summer home.

Underline the prepositional phrase in each sentence. Then write if it shows time, place, or direction.

6. We took photographs of the geese before they left their summer home. _____

7. The fawn slept beside its mother. _____

8. Salmon swim up the river to mate. _____

9. The snow begins to melt around April. _____

10. The migrating whales swam into the harbor. _____

Unit 2 • Reading 2

Writing — Write a Story with a Starter

Use with Student Edition pages 92–93.

Complete your own details chart using this story starter: "I arrived at the most amazing place." The setting could be a beach, a mountain peak, a desert, or a forest.

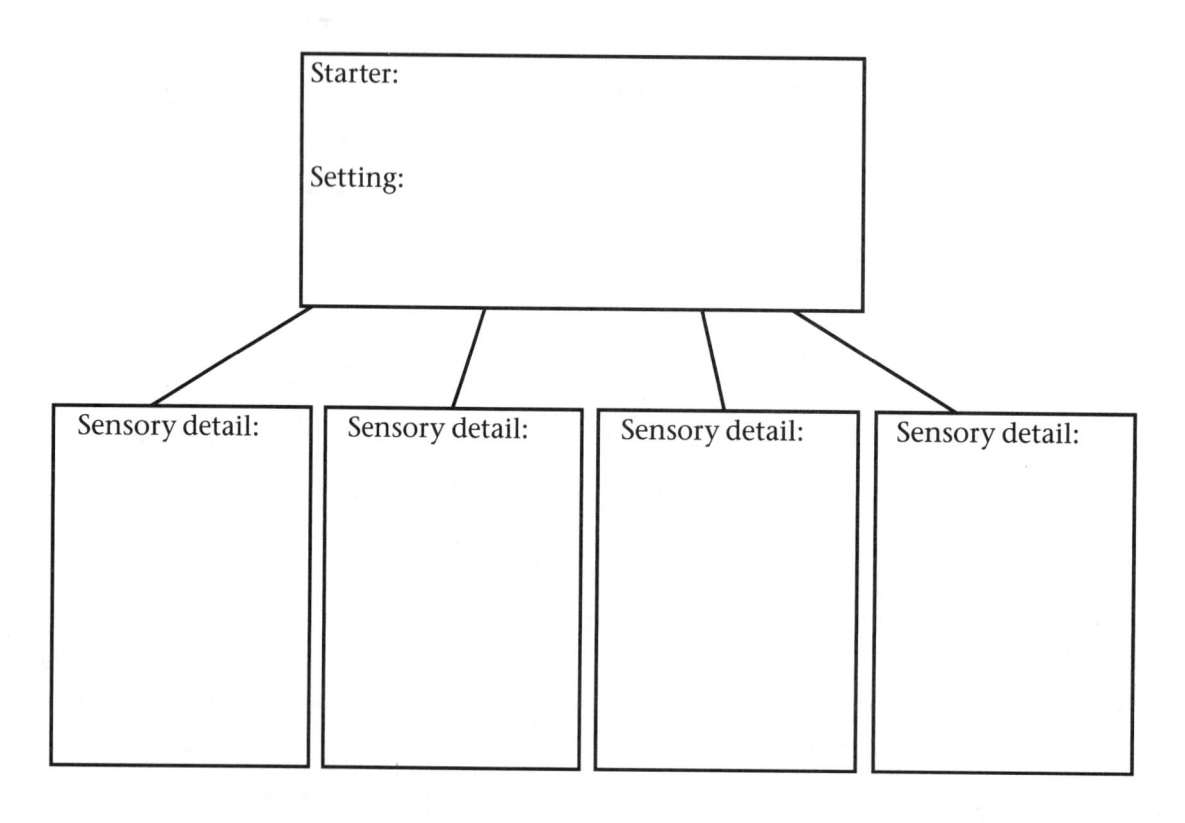

Starter:
Setting:

Sensory detail:	Sensory detail:	Sensory detail:	Sensory detail:

Have your partner complete (✓) the Peer Review Checklist. Use this feedback to help you edit your final draft.

Peer Review Checklist

- ☐ Does the story begin with one of the assigned starters?
- ☐ Does the story hold the reader's interest and attention?
- ☐ Are sensory details used to describe the setting?
- ☐ Are prepositions used correctly?
- ☐ Does the writer use parallel structure when appropriate?
- ☐ Could changes be made to improve the story?

Name _____ Date _____

UNIT 2

Where can a journey take you?

Reading 3: from *The Journal of Wong Ming-Chung*

Vocabulary **Literary Words** *Use with Student Edition page 95.*

REMEMBER A **simile** is a figure of speech that makes a comparison between two different things using the words *like* or *as*. **Example:** His shouting sounded like a barking dog. A **metaphor** is a figure of speech that writers use to describe something as if it were something else. **Example:** He barked his orders at us.

Next to each sentence, write *S* if it contains a simile and *M* if it contains a metaphor.

Example: He's a real live wire. _____M_____

1. She's as sharp as a tack. _____

2. The U.S.A. is a melting pot. _____

3. This game is a piece of cake. _____

4. He is like a bull in a china shop. _____

5. Love is as warm as a summer day. _____

Read the following story. Underline the similes and draw a circle around the metaphors.

All the Way to Grandma's House

My brother (Danny was a grasshopper) all the way to the airport. It seemed like he just couldn't sit still. I <u>sat still as a stone</u> as far from him and everyone else in my family as I could get. This trip was an unwelcome intruder into my summer plans. I love my grandparents, but spending two weeks at their farm seemed about as exciting as a cell phone with a dead battery.

Unit 2 • Reading 3   49

Vocabulary — **Academic Words** *Use with Student Edition page 96.*

Read the paragraph below. Pay attention to the underlined Academic Words.

> History books <u>emphasize</u> the importance of Ellis Island to the history of the United States. From 1892 to 1954, Ellis Island was a federal <u>immigration</u> station. It was the entry point to the United States for over 20 million immigrants. Ellis Island was a temporary home for many of the immigrants while they waited to be admitted into the country. When immigrants left Ellis Island, they were free to settle in the United States and begin to <u>adjust</u> to a new way of life. Many of them kept <u>journals</u> that describe what life was like in the U.S.A. at that time.

Write Academic Words from the paragraph next to their correct definitions.

Example: ___adjust___: make a change in something to make it better

1. _____: show that something is important

2. _____: a written record kept by an individual

3. _____: the act of going to live in another country

Use the Academic Words from the exercise above to complete the sentences.

4. Our teacher tried to _____ the importance of the field trip.

5. When there is a big change in your life, you have to _____.

6. Stella wrote in her _____ every day so she would remember everything that happened.

7. During the Irish potato famine, there was a big increase in _____ to the U.S.A.

Complete the sentences with your own ideas.

Example: The principal often emphasizes <u>that our school needs more classrooms</u>.

8. One of the results of immigration is _____.

9. This year, I had to adjust to _____.

10. One good reason for keeping a journal is because _____.

50   Unit 2 • Reading 3

Name _____ Date _____

Word Study — Words Ending in y *Use with Student Edition page 97.*

REMEMBER To change the spelling of certain **words that end in y**, change the *y* to *-i* and add *-es*. With comparative or superlative adjectives that end in *y*, change the *y* to *-ier* or *-iest*.

Complete the chart below by changing the *y* to *-i* and add *-es*, *-er*, or *-est*. Write the new words on the chart. An example is done for you.

Noun	Plural Noun
puppy	puppies
army	
party	
Verb	**Third-Person Singular Verb**
study	
carry	
supply	

Adjectives	Comparative	Superlative
friendly		
happy		
heavy		

Write the plural, third-person singular, comparative, or superlative form of the words as directed.

Example: library (plural) ___libraries___

1. berry (plural) _____
2. lucky (superlative) _____
3. theory (plural) _____
4. fancy (comparative) _____
5. baby (plural) _____
6. merry (comparative) _____
7. apply (3rd-person sing.) _____
8. funny (comparative) _____
9. city (plural) _____
10. copy (3rd-person sing.) _____

Unit 2 • Reading 3   51

> **Reading Strategy** Make Inferences

Use with Student Edition page 97.

REMEMBER Sometimes writers imply or suggest information, and readers must infer, or figure out, what the writer means.

Read the following story. Then answer the questions.

Auntie Ox

When my Aunt Oksana came from Russia to live with us, she came with almost nothing. I called her Auntie Ox because I couldn't pronounce her whole name. Auntie Ox always drank from a special cup she had brought with her from Russia. The cup was very old and we had plenty of new, nicer ones. Yet Auntie Ox always treated the old cup with great care. She kept it in a special place in the cabinet.

One day, I dropped the cup by accident. It broke into lots of little pieces. I felt badly because Auntie Ox cried. Even so, I did not understand why an old cup was so important to her. My parents said, "Maybe someday when you are older, you will understand."

Read the questions and explain how you used clues from the passage to make each inference.

1. From the passage, what do you infer about Auntie Ox's situation when she came to live with the narrator's family? Is Auntie Ox rich or poor?
   _____

2. Why do you think the cup means so much to Auntie Ox?
   _____

3. Why do you think Auntie Ox was so upset when the old cup broke?
   _____

4. Why do you think the narrator cannot understand Auntie Ox's tears over an old cup?
   _____

5. What do you think the narrator's parents mean when they say that the narrator will understand Auntie Ox's tears someday?
   _____

Name _____ Date _____

Comprehension Use with Student Edition page 104.

Choose the best answer for each item. Circle the letter of the correct answer.

1. The narrator calls San Francisco _____.

    a. First City   **b.** the Golden Mountain   **c.** the Big Pond

2. Chinese people in San Francisco were grouped by their _____.

    a. areas   **b.** occupations   **c.** initials

3. The narrator was amazed at mealtime because he _____.

    a. had no food   **b.** had to share food   **c.** had a lot of good food

4. The narrator felt proud of the city's first stone building because _____.

    a. it was built by Chinese workers   **b.** the instructions were in Chinese   **c.** it was an American building

5. The narrator felt right at home in Chinatown because _____.

    a. he lived on the second floor   **b.** Blessing was there, too   **c.** it smelled like incense and food

Response to Literature Use with Student Edition page 105.

Find a paragraph in the story that reminds you of an experience in your own life. Tell about your experience and explain why the paragraph reminds you of it.

_____
_____
_____
_____
_____
_____
_____

Unit 2 • Reading 3

Grammar: Complex Sentences with Adverbial Clauses of Time

Use with Student Edition page 106.

> **REMEMBER** **Complex sentences** contain an independent clause and at least one dependent clause. An **adverbial clause** of time is a dependent clause and begins with a subordinate conjunction, such as *after, before, when, as soon as,* or *whenever*. When an adverbial clause of time begins the sentence, it is followed by a comma.

Underline the adverbial clause of time in each sentence. Then circle the subordinate conjunction.

Example: Baseball practice is cancelled (whenever) it rains.

1. Before I bought a bicycle, I walked everywhere.
2. She became stronger as soon as she started lifting weights.
3. When you play basketball, you improve your coordination.
4. He likes to listen to music whenever he studies.
5. After I walk my dog, I usually do my homework.

Put a ✓ next to the sentences that have correct punctuation. Put an X next to the sentences that do not. Then add commas where necessary.

Example: __X__ When the sun is shining, I like to be outside.

_____ 6. You can't go skiing when it doesn't snow.

_____ 7. After we got home we ate a large meal.

_____ 8. Before I visited San Francisco I went to Los Angeles.

_____ 9. It rained when we were in the mountains.

_____ 10. As soon as my mom gets home we can go to the mall.

Name _____ Date _____

Grammar — Expressions of Quantity and Subject-Verb Agreement

Use with Student Edition page 107.

> **REMEMBER** You can use **expressions of quantity** to tell about three or more items. *All, most, some, a lot of,* and *none of the* can be used with count or non-count nouns. When used with count nouns, they take plural subjects and verbs; when used with non-count nouns, they take singular verbs. *A few, many,* and *several* are always used with count nouns and take plural subjects and verbs. *A little* is always used with non-count nouns and takes a singular verb. When referring to a specific group, use the expression of quantity with *of the*. **Example:** Many of the men work here.

Complete each sentence by circling all the correct expressions of quantity.

Example: (All) / Several / (None) of the milk sold in this supermarket is from a local dairy.

1. (A little / Several / A few) bridges connect the island to the mainland.
2. (Most / Some / A few) gasoline sold in the U.S.A. comes from foreign countries.
3. (A few / Most / A little) of the science projects must be completed by next week.
4. (Many / A few / A little) of the mountains were covered with snow.
5. I spilled (some / a little / many) coffee on the table.

Write sentences with the expressions of quantity in parentheses.

Example: (many) _____ Many students go to my school. _____

6. (some) _____
7. (all) _____
8. (none of the) _____

Writing **Write a Personal Letter** *Use with Student Edition pages 108–109.*

Complete your own graphic organizer for a letter to a friend or family member about an event. List your ideas in chronological order.

```
                                                              Date

   Salutation
   or Greeting,

   ┌──────────────────────────────────────────────────────┐
   │ Body                                                 │
   │                                                      │
   │                                                      │
   │                                                      │
   │                                                      │
   └──────────────────────────────────────────────────────┘

                                                           Closing,
                                                         Signature
```

Have your partner complete (✓) the Peer Review Checklist. Use this feedback to help you edit your final draft.

Peer Review Checklist
- [ ] Is the letter addressed to a friend or relative?
- [ ] Is it informal and friendly in tone?
- [ ] Does it express the writer's feelings?
- [ ] Does it include all five parts of a friendly letter?
- [ ] Are adverbial clauses of time used correctly?
- [ ] Could changes be made to improve the letter?

Name _____ Date _____

Writing Workshop *Use with Student Edition pages 114–118.*

Organize your ideas in the graphic organizer below.

Who are the characters?	Where and when is the story set?	What is the problem?	What is the resolution?

Have your partner complete (✓) the Peer Review Checklist. Use this feedback to help you edit your final draft.

Peer Review Checklist

- ☐ Does the story sustain my interest?
- ☐ Is the story engaging?
- ☐ Is the action well paced?
- ☐ Is the setting specific and believable?
- ☐ Are the characters interesting? Are they well developed?
- ☐ Could changes be made to improve the story?

Unit 2 • Writing Workshop

Learning Log *Use after completing Student Edition page 118.*

Underline the vocabulary items you know and can use well. Review and practice any you haven't underlined. Underline them when you know them well.

Literary Words	Key Words	Academic Words	
character plot point of view simile metaphor	biologists herd landscape magnetic range starvation	abandon attribute finally react approaches approximate area migrate	adjust emphasize immigration journal

Put a check by the skills you can perform well. Review and practice any you haven't checked off. Check them off when you can perform them well.

Skills	I can . . .
Word Study	☐ recognize the roots *vict, laps, mem, mand*. ☐ recognize words used as multiple parts of speech. ☐ recognize words ending in *y*.
Reading Strategies	☐ identify problems and solutions. ☐ recognize cause and effect. ☐ make inferences.
Grammar	☐ use the simple past of regular and irregular verbs. ☐ use pronouns and modifiers in simple sentences. ☐ use parallel structure. ☐ use prepositions in prepositional phrases. ☐ use adverbial clauses of time. ☐ use expressions of quantity and subject-verb agreement.
Writing	☐ write a story from a different point of view. ☐ write a story with a starter. ☐ write a personal letter. ☐ write a short story.

Name _____ Date _____

Test Preparation

Test 1

DIRECTIONS
Read this selection. Then answer the questions that follow it.

Bats on the Congress Avenue Bridge

(1) My cousins are visiting from Ohio, but tonight we have a special treat planned. (2) Were leaving at 8 o'clock to go to the Congress Avenue Bridge. (3) I told my cousins, Jed and Lisa, that over a million bats live in the colony under the bridge.

(4) At sunset, what looked like black smoke rose from under the bridge. (5) Lisa started to cry. (6) "They're going to eat me!" she cried. (7) "Not unless you're a mosquito" I said.

1. What change, if any, should be made to sentence 1?
   A Delete the comma
   B Change *but* to *and*
   C Change *have* to *had*
   D Make no change

2. What change, if any, should be made to sentence 2?
   A Change *o'clock* to *oclock*
   B Change *Were* to *Where*
   C Change *Were* to *We're*
   D Make no change

3. What change, if any, should be made to sentence 7?
   A Change *you're* to *your*
   B Change *mosquito* to *mosqitos*
   C Insert a comma after *mosquito*
   D Make no change

Test Preparation 59

Test 2

DIRECTIONS
Read this selection. Then answer the questions that follow it.

> *Maria wrote this paper for her science class. Maria would like you to read her rough draft and decide how to correct and improve it.*
>
> ## Bats
>
> (1) Bats are important animals. (2) They help the environment. (3) They eat insects that fly at night, especially mosquitoes. (4) They can eat half their body wait in bugs every night. (5) A single bat can eat 3,000 insects at night. (6) Second, even though most bat species eat insects, other bat species eat fruits. (7) This helps the environment because the bats spread seeds of trees and shrubs. (8) New seeds keep forests healthy. (9) Finally, bats pollinate flowers. (10) If it weren't for bats there would be more bugs and fewer flowers.

1 What transition word should be added to sentence 3?
  A First
  B To begin with
  C However
  D In conclusion

2 What change should be made in sentence 4?
  A Change *eat* to **eats**
  B Change *wait* to **weight**
  C Add a comma
  D Make no change

3 What revision, if any, is needed in sentence 7?
  A Add a comma
  B Change *seeds* to **seads**
  C Change *spread* to **spreads**
  D Make no change

4 What revision, if any, is needed in sentence 10?
  A Change *would be* to **be**
  B Change *flowers* to **flours**
  C Add a comma after *bats*
  D Make no change

Test 3

DIRECTIONS
Read this selection. Then answer the questions that follow it.

Luca wrote this paper for an assignment in his social studies class. Luca would like you to read his rough draft and suggest corrections and improvements.

Magnificent Machu Picchu

(1) The city of Machu Picchu, located high in the andes mountains, is one of the world's most incredible historical sites. (2) In the 1400s, the Incas built a stone city that covered five square miles and included palaces, temples and nearly 200 homes. (3) The massive granite blocks used to build these structures weighed up to fifty tons, so the Incas fitted the blocks so strongly that the structures still stand today. (4) In fact, the blocks fit together so well that it is impossible to insert even a knife blade between them. (5) The people living in the city provides for their own food. (6) They grew corn, potatoes and other vegetables. (7) They used methods such as irrigation, or watering systems. (8) Machu Picchu was also an astronomical observatory. (9) This means the Incas went there to look at the stars. (10) The Incas used a special stone, called the Hitching Post of the Sun, to show important dates in their calendar. (11) The Incas left the mountain city in the late 1500s following the spanish overthrow of the Incan Empire. (12) The Spanish never found the city. (13) It was undisturbed until 1911, when Hiram Bingham rediscovered it.

1 What change should be made in sentence 1?
  A Change *world's* to **worlds**
  B Remove a comma
  C Change *andes* to **Andes**
  D Change *is* to **are**

2 What change, if any, should be made in sentence 2?
  A Add a comma after *temples*
  B Change *temples* to **timples**
  C Change *included* to **includes**
  D Make no change

Test Preparation

3 What is the *best* way to revise sentence 3?

  A The massive granite blocks used to build these structures weighed up to fifty tons, and the Incas fitted these blocks so strongly that the structures still stands today.

  B The massive granite blocks used to build these structures weighed up to fifty tons; but the Incas fitted the blocks so strongly that the structures still stand today.

  C The massive granite blocks used to build these structures weighed up to fifty tons. And the Incas fitted the blocks so strongly that the structures still stand today.

  D No revision is needed

4 What revisions, if any, should be made in sentence 5?

  A Change *their* to **our**
  B Add a comma
  C Change *provides* to **provided**
  D Make no revision

5 What change should be made in sentence 6?

  A Add a comma after *potatoes*
  B Change *potatoes* to *potatos*
  C Change *grew* to **will grow**
  D Change *vegetable* to **vegetables**

6 What change, if any, should be made in sentence 11?

  A Add a comma
  B change *spanish* to **Spanish**
  C change *following* to **follow**
  D Make no change

Name _____ Date _____

Visual Literacy: Smithsonian American
Art Museum *Use with Student Edition pages 120–121.*

Learning to Look

Look at *Electronic Superhighway: Continental U.S., Alaska, Hawaii* by Nam June Paik on page 121 in your Student Edition. List six types of lines or shapes you see in this artwork.

Example: _____straight line_____

1. _____   4. _____
2. _____   5. _____
3. _____   6. _____

Interpretation

Look at *Electronic Superhighway: Continental U.S., Alaska, Hawaii* again. Imagine that the artist is going to make a video for your country. Write him a letter explaining what he should include and why it represents your country.

Example: I live in Venezuela. I think Paik should include a photograph of Angel Falls because it is so amazing and many tourists visit it.

Dear Mr. Paik,

_____

_____

_____

_____

_____

_____

_____

Compare & Contrast

How does Nam June Paik's map compare to another map you have seen? For example, look at a map of the U.S.A. in an atlas or on the internet.

How are they similar?

1. _____
2. _____
3. _____

How are they different?

Example: The tip of Texas is missing on Paik's map.

4. _____
5. _____
6. _____

Name _____ Date _____

UNIT 3: What defines success?

Reading 1: "Success Stories"

Vocabulary — **Key Words** *Use with Student Edition page 125.*

Write each word in the box next to its definition.

| enterprise | excelled | famine | satellite | scholarships | ~~self-portrait~~ |

Example: <u>self-portrait</u>: a picture that you make of yourself

1. _____: a time of hunger and lack of food
2. _____: the ability to work hard and think of new ideas
3. _____: money awarded to pay for students' education
4. _____: did something better than others
5. _____: a machine or device sent into space to orbit around Earth

Use words from the word box to complete the sentences below.

6. The hard-working students won _____ to very good colleges.
7. When it does not rain for many years, there may be a _____ because little food can be grown.
8. The girl _____ in science and won first prize at the science fair.
9. Because of the _____ and vision of many people, we have a unique and successful community center.
10. The artist won an award for his realistic _____.

Unit 3 • Reading 1

Vocabulary

Academic Words *Use with Student Edition page 126.*

Read the paragraph below. Pay attention to the underlined Academic Words.

> Our school made a <u>commitment</u> to help hurricane victims in the Caribbean. We thought of ways we could provide <u>aid</u> to the people who were suffering. My class made it a <u>priority</u> to collect items to send to people who had lost their homes. The smallest contribution, such as blankets or canned food, can make a difference. We are all part of a <u>global</u> community, and we should help others in the world who are suffering.

Match each word with its definition.

Example: __b__ aid

____ 1. priority

____ 2. commitment

____ 3. global

a. a promise and a determination to do something

b. assistance, especially in the form of money, food, or equipment

c. affecting or relating to the whole world

d. the thing that you think is most important

Use the Academic Words from the exercise above to complete the sentences.

4. I made a(n) _____ to help at the animal shelter, and I've kept it.

5. Having fun with friends is important, but getting good grades is my top _____.

6. Of all the countries in the world, the United States gives the most _____ to poor and struggling countries.

7. I think the environment is a(n) _____ issue because it affects people everywhere on Earth.

Complete the sentences with your own ideas.

Example: I have a strong commitment to __my family and friends__.

8. A top priority in my life is _____.

9. The best aid we can give to people who manage to survive natural disasters is _____.

Name _____ Date _____

Word Study Prefixes *under-, re-, multi-, inter-*

Use with Student Edition page 127.

> **REMEMBER** A **prefix** is a letter or group of letters added to the beginning of a word to change its meaning. The prefix *under-* means *below*, as in *underwater*. The prefix *re-* means *again*, as in *replay*. The prefix *multi-* means *many*, as in *multimedia*. The prefix *inter-* means *between*, as in *interact*.

Look at the chart. Add the prefix *under-, re-, multi-,* or *inter-* to the words in order to create new words. Write the new words on the chart.

Word	Prefix	New Word	Definition
foot	under-	underfoot	below the foot or feet
1. paid	under-		
2. paint	re-		
3. colored	multi-		
4. state	inter-		
5. run	re-		

Create new words by adding the prefix *under-, re-, multi-,* or *inter-*. Check a dictionary, if needed. Then write the definition next to the new word.

Example: gain __regain: gain again__

6. cooked _____

7. place _____

8. purpose _____

9. section _____

10. send _____

11. national _____

Unit 3 • Reading 1

Reading Strategy | **Connect Ideas**

Use with Student Edition page 127.

> **REMEMBER** When you read informational texts, try to **connect ideas**. Think about the main ideas in the different texts. What do they have in common? How are they similar? For each of these biographies, identify the person it is about. Then decide what the main idea and key details are.

Read the paragraphs below. Circle the name of the person each one is about. Underline main ideas and key details about the person.

1. Langston Hughes was born in Missouri, U.S.A. in 1902. As a young man, he moved to the neighborhood of Harlem in New York City. In the 1920s, many of the most brilliant African-American artists and writers lived in Harlem. Hughes was the best poet in Harlem. His poems were mainly about the lives of African-American people at that time. He also wrote plays, novels, and children's books. Langston Hughes is considered one of the greatest poets and writers in U.S. history.

2. A mural is a large painting that is painted on a wall. One of the best mural artists who ever lived was Diego Rivera. Rivera first painted murals in his native Mexico. His murals showed the life of the Mexican people, particularly poor people. Rivera used his art to try to improve the life of poor people in Mexico and elsewhere. When he became famous, he was hired to paint murals in different countries around the world.

3. Rachel Carson was a wildlife biologist in the 1950s. In her work, she saw that many birds were dying or disappearing. She found that some bug-killing chemicals were destroying the birds' eggs. Therefore, no baby birds were being born. Carson wrote a book about what she found. The book is called *Silent Spring*. The book was so popular that the U.S. government decided to take action. It stopped the use of these bug-killing chemicals. Rachel Carson never became rich, but her life's work helped save an important part of our natural world.

Answer the questions based on the paragraphs you've just read.

4. What do all three of the people mentioned above have in common?

   _____

   _____

5. How can you connect the ideas in the three texts? What is similar about the work of the three individuals?

   _____

   _____

Name _____ Date _____

Comprehension Use with Student Edition page 132.

Choose the best answer for each item. Circle the letter of the correct answer.

1. In her life and work, Frida Kahlo showed how much she loved Mexican _____.

    a. cocoa b. tradition c. food

2. Frida Kahlo was a great artist in spite of polio and of health problems that were caused by a terrible _____.

    a. storm b. exhibit c. accident

3. Bill Gates is a billionaire who donates a great deal of money to help eliminate _____.

    a. vaccines b. malaria c. software

4. Muhammad Yunus wanted to do something practical, so he helped very poor people by giving them _____.

    a. loans b. food c. cows

5. Mae Jemison succeeded in becoming the first female African-American _____.

    a. doctor b. president c. astronaut

Extension Use with Student Edition page 133.

Write five careers you might like to have when you grow up. Then write how you can succeed or help others by doing this work.

Career I'd Like to Have	How I Can Succeed or Help Others
doctor	cure sick people

Unit 3 • Reading 1

Grammar: Complex Sentences with Restrictive Adjectival Clauses

Use with Student Edition page 134.

> **REMEMBER** Adjectival clauses describe nouns. They begin with relative pronouns, such as *who* (to refer to people), *that* (to refer to things), or *where* (to refer to places). A **restrictive adjectival clause** is essential to the meaning of the sentence. Don't use commas with restrictive adjectival clauses.

Underline the restrictive adjectival clause in the sentence. Then circle the noun that the adjectival clause describes.

Example: Malaria is (a disease) that kills millions of people every year.

1. His computer is the one device that he can't live without.
2. The Baltic Sea is the place where you can find a lot of amber washed up on the shore.
3. A loan officer is the person who gives you the money from the bank.
4. My aunt writes the popular cookbooks that teach kids how to cook.
5. Green is the color that is used most in that painting.

Complete the sentences with *who*, *that*, or *where*.

Example: Landscape architects are people ___who___ design gardens.

6. My favorite books are the ones _____ describe important discoveries.
7. I have been reading about the vaccine _____ prevents polio.
8. Kyoto is the city _____ I've always wanted to live.
9. The movie is about the people _____ helped build the railroad.
10. Is the Amazon rainforest the place _____ you'd like to go this summer?

Name _____ Date _____

Complex Sentences with Nonrestrictive Adjectival Clauses
Use with Student Edition page 135.

> **REMEMBER** A **nonrestrictive adjectival clause** is not essential to the main idea of a sentence. Use commas with nonrestrictive clauses. You can use *who* to refer to people and *where* to refer to places in nonrestrictive clauses, but don't use *that* to refer to things. Instead, use *which* to refer to things in a nonrestrictive clause.

Decide if the adverbial clause in each sentence is restrictive or nonrestrictive. Then add commas around the nonrestrictive adjectival clauses.

Example: _nonrestrictive_ Hawaii, which consists of eight main islands, is a popular vacation spot.

1. _____ I ran into Ms. Loar who works at the bank.

2. _____ The glass that was in the cabinet is broken.

3. _____ Glass which is made chiefly from sand is a very useful material.

4. _____ Yuri is the banker who lends money to poor people.

5. _____ The pizza that we had for lunch was very good.

6. _____ Mr. Greene who teaches biology is an excellent instructor.

7. _____ I live in a town where there isn't much to do.

8. _____ The Shenandoah National Park where you can mountain bike is not far from my house.

9. _____ The students who finished the test could leave early, but the others had to stay.

10. _____ The article was about a man who died of a rare disease.

Unit 3 • Reading 1

Writing — **Write a Compare-and-Contrast Paragraph**

Use with Student Edition pages 136–137.

Complete your own Venn diagram about two places or people you know.

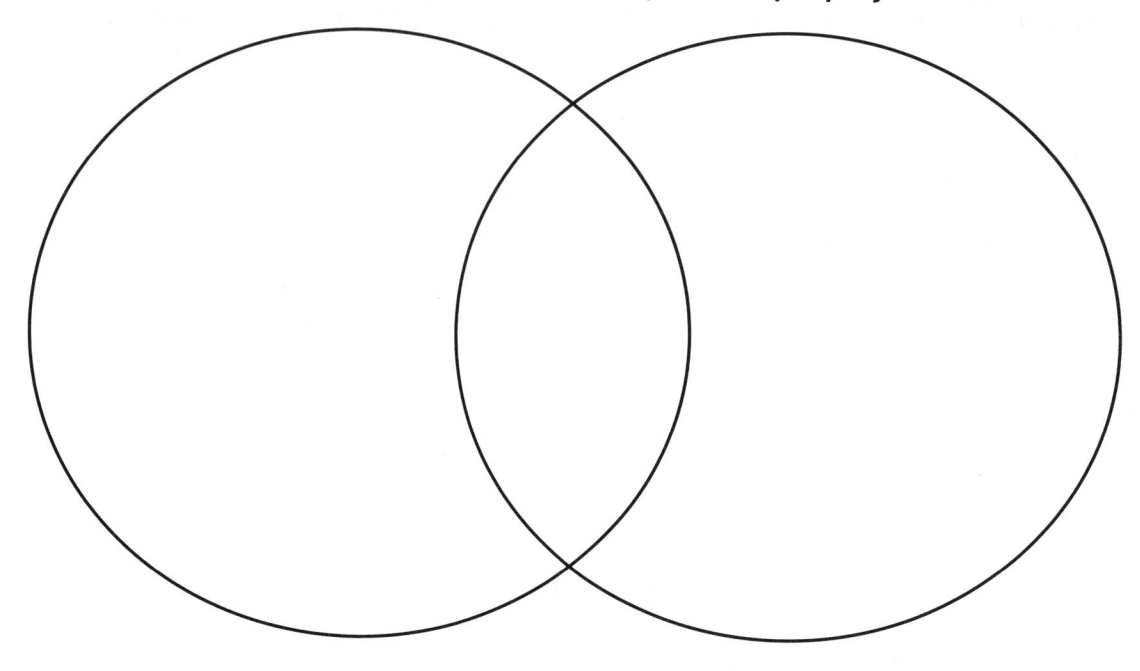

Have your partner complete (✓) the Peer Review Checklist. Use this feedback to help you edit your final draft.

Peer Review Checklist

- ☐ Does the paragraph compare two people or places?
- ☐ Are similarities and differences presented in a logical order?
- ☐ Does the writer use signal words such as *also*, *too*, *although*, and *but*?
- ☐ Do sentences vary in length and pattern?
- ☐ Are restrictive and nonrestrictive clauses used correctly?
- ☐ Could changes be made to improve the paragraph?

Name _____ Date _____

UNIT 3: What defines success?

Reading 2: "If" / "A Game of Hide and Seek"

Vocabulary — **Literary Words** *Use with Student Edition page 139.*

> **REMEMBER** A **metaphor** is a figure of speech in which one thing is spoken of as though it were something else. An **extended metaphor** continues the comparison for several lines or for an entire poem. Writers use **repetition** of words and phrases to emphasize ideas. A **stanza** is a group of lines in a poem.

Read the items. Label each one *extended metaphor*, *repetition*, or *stanza*.

metaphor	My children are my sunshine.
1.	We thought the movie was dull, dull, dull.
2.	'Twas the night before Christmas when all through the house Not a creature was stirring, not even a mouse; The stockings were hung by the chimney with care In hopes that St. Nicholas soon would be there.
3.	He was just a young man, but a young man with dreams; a young man with vision.
4.	The car was a monster that roared and clanked down the street, scaring the shoppers.

5. Write a one-stanza poem about what you want to be when you are an adult. Use repetition or an extended metaphor in your stanza.

_____
_____
_____
_____

Unit 3 • Reading 2

Vocabulary — **Academic Words** *Use with Student Edition page 140.*

Read the paragraph below. Pay attention to the underlined Academic Words.

> I want to pursue my interest in ancient Egypt someday. I know that Egypt is known for its pyramids, which contained the mummies of Egyptian kings. To me, the pyramids are the most distinctive monuments in the world. Inside many pyramids are hieroglyphs, a type of writing. It took many years for scientists to interpret the precise meaning of these symbols. We have learned much about the Egyptians from their hieroglyphs. And I am determined to find out more!

Write Academic Words from the paragraph above next to their correct definitions.

Example: ___pursue___: to continue doing an activity or trying to achieve something

1. _____: to explain or translate
2. _____: exact and correct in every detail
3. _____: clearly marking a person or thing as different from others

Use the Academic Words from the paragraph to complete the sentences.

4. You can easily identify this flower by its _____ shape and color.
5. In science, you must be very _____ when you conduct an experiment.
6. She is determined to _____ her love of gymnastics.
7. He doesn't speak Japanese and she doesn't speak English, so I will _____ for them.

Complete the sentences with your own ideas.

Example: Different countries have distinctive ___food, clothing, holidays, and values___.

8. I'd like to pursue my dream of _____.
9. It's important to be precise when you are _____.
10. To interpret a poet's meaning, it helps to understand _____.

Unit 3 • Reading 2

Name _____ Date _____

Word Study **Homophones** *Use with Student Edition page 141.*

REMEMBER A **homophone** is a word that sounds the same as another word but has a different meaning. The homophones may or may not be spelled the same. For example, *weather* and *whether* are homophones. *Weather* means "climate"; *whether* means "if." You can use a dictionary to help you determine the spelling and meaning of homophones.

Write definitions for each pair of homophones in the chart.

Words	Definitions
bore, boar	tiresome person; wild pig
1. bread, bred	
2. buy, by	
3. cell, sell	
4. your, you're	
5. hour, our	

Write a definition for each pair of homophones. Use a dictionary if needed. Then use both words in a sentence that shows their meaning.

Example: reeds, reads stalks of marsh grass; interprets the written word
He reads a book about the reeds in the marsh.

6. do, due _____
_____

7. fare, fair _____
_____

8. it's, its _____
_____

9. meet, meat _____
_____

10. presence, presents _____
_____

Unit 3 • Reading 2

Reading Strategy: Identify Author's Purpose

Use with Student Edition page 141.

> **REMEMBER** When you read a work of literature, it helps to **identify the author's purpose** for writing it. We often think of informational articles or persuasive ads when we think of the author's purpose, but poetry has a purpose, too. Understanding the author's purpose will help you understand a poem.

Read the following poems and decide the author's purpose. There may be more than one.

entertain	express a feeling	tell a story	get a particular reaction from the reader
	make the reader think deeply about a subject		

"Clay" by James Joyce
I dreamt that I dwelt in marble halls
    With vassals and serfs at my side
And of all who assembled within those walls
    That I was the hope and the pride.
I had riches too great to count, could boast
    Of a high ancestral name,
But I also dreamt, which pleased me most,
    That you loved me still the same.

1. What is the author's purpose? _____

"A Limerick" by Edward Lear
There was an Old Man with a beard,
Who said, "It is just as I feared!—
Two Owls and a Hen,
Four Larks and a Wren,
Have all built their nests in my beard!"

2. What is the author's purpose? _____

Excerpt from "On the Road to the Sea" by Charlotte Mew
We passed each other, turned and stopped for half an hour, then went our way,
    I who make other women smile did not make you—
But no man can move mountains in a day.
    So this hard thing is yet to do.

3. What is the author's purpose? _____

4. Imagine you are writing a poem to make the reader think deeply about your favorite animal. Write the first two lines of the poem. They do not have to rhyme.

_____

_____

Name _____ Date _____

Comprehension   Use with Student Edition page 146.

Choose the best answer for each item. Circle the letter of the correct answer.

1. The speaker in "If" is talking to his _____.

    a. father b. son c. grandson

2. The speaker in "If" says that if you lose, you should _____.

    a. try again b. try to win money c. risk your life

3. In the first four stanzas of "A Game of Hide and Seek," what does *it* refer to?

    a. a cat b. poetry c. success

4. According to "A Game of Hide and Seek," you will find success if you _____.

    a. spend time in nature b. try lots of different things c. do the things you love to do

5. Both "If" and "A Game of Hide and Seek" were written to _____.

    a. give comfort when something has gone wrong b. offer advice about living your life to its fullest c. warn the listener about dangers in the future

Response to Literature   Use with Student Edition page 147.

"A Game of Hide and Seek" uses an extended metaphor to talk about success. What is success to you? Is it something you have to build, a race you must finish, or a garden you need to nurture? Use your own ideas to write a poem about success that uses an extended metaphor.

Your purpose: _____

Extended metaphor: _____

Title of your poem: _____

Lines in your poem: _____

_____

_____

_____

Unit 3 • Reading 2

Grammar: Gerunds as Subjects *Use with Student Edition page 148.*

REMEMBER A **gerund**, the *-ing* form of the verb, functions as a noun. A gerund or gerund phrase can be the subject of a sentence. A possessive noun or pronoun often comes before and modifies a gerund. When a gerund is the subject, it is singular and is followed by a third-person-singular verb. Use *not* before a gerund to make it negative.

Complete the chart with the gerund form of each verb.

Base Form	Gerund
1. see	
2. swim	
3. smile	
4. make	
5. work	

Complete the sentences with the gerund form of the verbs in parentheses.

Example: (fix) _____Fixing_____ cars is my father's hobby.

6. (read) _____ novels is a good way to improve your vocabulary.

7. His piano (play) _____ has improved greatly.

8. My aunt's (bake) _____ is remarkable.

9. (not know) _____ the language spoken in your favorite vacation spot can be a problem.

10. (take) _____ a hot bath always relaxes me.

Name _____ Date _____

Gerunds as Objects after Verbs and Prepositions
Use with Student Edition page 149.

> **REMEMBER** A **gerund** can also be the object of a verb in a sentence. Certain verbs, such as *start*, *understand*, and *like*, are often followed by gerunds. Gerunds can also be objects of prepositions.

Complete the sentences with the gerund form of the verbs in parentheses. Then underline the verbs that precede the gerunds and circle the prepositions.

Example: My mother <u>started</u> (sew) __*sewing*__ curtains (for) the living
room windows.

1. When he started (grin) _____, we knew he understood the joke.

2. I remembered (be) _____ there when I was about eight years old.

3. Would you consider (make) _____ a video of your family's vacation?

4. We were tired from (walk) _____ all day.

5. I enjoy (not have) _____ to get up early on the weekends.

6. The movie was about (live) _____ in a new colony on another planet.

7. She enjoyed (work) _____ at her family's bakery after school.

8. We enjoyed (go) _____ to the soccer tournament.

Writing: Write a Problem-and-Solution Paragraph

Use with Student Edition pages 150–151.

Complete your own idea web about a problem you want to solve.

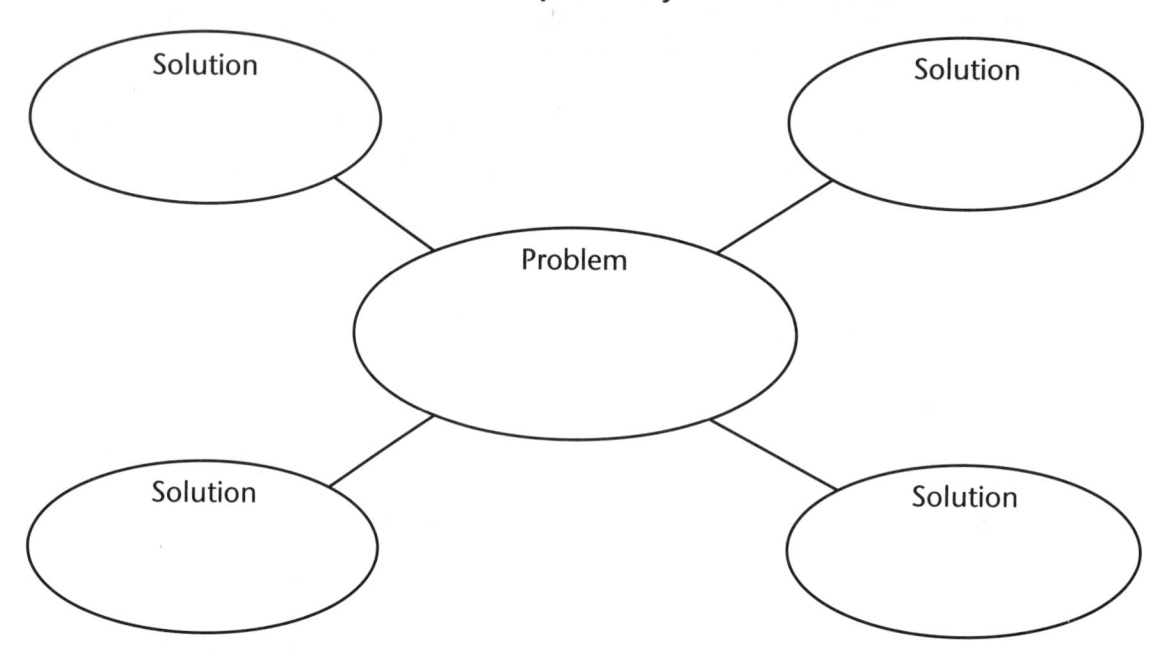

- Solution
- Solution
- Problem
- Solution
- Solution

Have your partner complete (✓) the Peer Review Checklist. Use this feedback to help you edit your final draft.

Peer Review Checklist

- ☐ Does the paragraph focus on a problem and solution?
- ☐ Does it hold the reader's interest and attention?
- ☐ Are solutions explained with specificity and detail?
- ☐ Does the writer use the right words for the topic?
- ☐ Are gerunds used correctly as subjects and objects?
- ☐ Could changes be made to improve the paragraph?

Name _____ Date _____

UNIT 3: What defines success?

Reading 3: "The Marble Champ"

Vocabulary | **Literary Words** Use with Student Edition page 153.

> **REMEMBER** As you read, notice **character motivation** to understand why a character feels, acts, and behaves in a certain way. Also notice **suspense** that a writer may use to create a feeling of excitement or to make you wonder what will happen next.

Read each sentence. Label each sentence with the term that describes it: *character motivation* or *suspense*.

suspense	We heard the sound of footsteps coming closer and closer, but it was dark and we had no idea who it could be.
1.	Carlos looked longingly at his brother's trophies and then, he decided what he was going to do.
2.	The man walked through the grass, unaware that the snake was creeping closer and closer.
3.	Amy looked at her test score, ripped it up, and told no one about it.
4.	The judge announced that it was time to find out who the winner of the competition was.

5. Read the following passage. Underline the words, phrases, and sentences that create suspense.

> Maria had been so kind, and I didn't want her to leave before I had a chance to thank her. I had to tell Maria the news, but she was already at the train station. I only had two minutes to reach her before she got on the train. I put the key into the car's ignition, but the engine would not start. I tried the ignition again and again. All the while, I could hear the sound of the train in the distance. If the car didn't start, I would not reach Maria in time! I tried the engine once more. Finally, without a moment to spare, the car started. I raced off into the night.

Vocabulary — Academic Words *Use with Student Edition page 154.*

Read the paragraph below. Pay attention to the underlined Academic Words.

> Emily had <u>considerable</u> skill in spelling. She had won second place in the school Spelling Bee the <u>previous</u> year. Her <u>objective</u> this year was to win first place. She studied for weeks so she would be ready to <u>participate</u>. After a tough competition, she won first place!

Match each word with its definition.

Example: __b__ previous   **a.** be involved in a particular activity

_____ 1. considerable   **b.** happening before something else

_____ 2. objective   **c.** large enough to be noticed or have an effect

_____ 3. participate   **d.** goal; something that you are working hard to achieve

Use the Academic Words from the exercise above to complete the sentences.

4. She put _____ effort into practicing her guitar and singing.

5. Her _____ was to enter the local talent show.

6. At the town's community center, she filled out a form so that she could _____ in the talent show.

Complete the sentences with your own ideas.

Example: Things that have a considerable effect on my life are _my family, my friends, my classmates, and my neighborhood_.

7. Some activities I would like to participate in are _____ _____.

8. Two objectives I would like to achieve this year are _____ _____.

9. We went to the yard sale and found some things that the previous owners _____.

Name _____ Date _____

Word Study — Inflections *-ed* and *-ing* Use with Student Edition page 155.

REMEMBER Some words have **inflected endings**. These add a different meaning to a base word. Some words have the inflections *-ed* or *-ing* added at the end. In base words with a short vowel before the final consonant, the final consonant is doubled when *-ed* or *-ing* is added, as in *winning*.

Look at the chart. Add *-ed* or *-ing* to the words. Write the new words in the correct column of the chart.

Base Word	Inflection *-ed*	Inflection *-ing*
Example: plan	planned	planning
1. allow		
2. ship		
3. walk		
4. occur		
5. borrow		

Write the base form of the inflected words below.

Example: texted   _____text_____

6. called   _____

7. phoning   _____

8. emailed   _____

9. tapping   _____

10. typed   _____

Reading Strategy: Predict 2

Use with Student Edition page 155.

> **REMEMBER** To **predict** means to guess what will happen in a story. When you predict, you understand a story better. Predicting also helps you focus on the story. You can make predictions before you read and change them as you're reading.

Read the paragraphs below. Underline the clues you can use to make a prediction. Circle information that might make you change your prediction.

1. Yu Yan had followed the cake recipe carefully and put the batter in the oven to bake. The baking batter smelled so good, she knew the cake would be delicious. Then the phone rang. It was her best friend. Yu Yan and her friend talked and talked. Suddenly, Yu Yan smelled something burning.

2. Joao was studying for a big history test. The test was the next morning at 8:30 a.m. The night before, Joao studied hour after hour. The next thing he knew, he was opening his eyes. It was 8 a.m. He'd fallen asleep—and he hadn't finished studying for the test!

3. On the Saturday of the picnic, a group of friends were eager for the drive to the country. The day was glorious and sunny. They could not wait to go for a swim. This would be one of the best days of the summer. They were all going for a swim in the lake, when suddenly, the day grew dark and a deep clap of thunder sounded and rumbled across the sky.

Read each paragraph and predict what will happen next. Then, answer the question.

4. Luana was the fastest runner in school. The race started, and everyone cheered. Luana easily took the lead. As the runners circled the track, Luana was out front, ahead of everyone else. Her schoolmates yelled and cheered as she neared the finish line.

   What do you predict will happen next?

   _____

5. When Luana was only about 20 feet from the finish line, a runner from the opposing team started to gain on her. Luana sensed that the other runner might catch up to her. Then Luana made a terrible mistake.

   How would you change the prediction you made for question 4?

   _____

Name _____ Date _____

Comprehension Use with Student Edition page 164.

Choose the best answer for each item. Circle the letter of the best answer.

1. To do well at marbles, Lupe had to strengthen her _____.

   a. thumb   b. arms   c. feet

2. Lupe became a good marbles player by spending a lot of time _____.

   a. doing push-ups b. practicing   c. studying

3. Though he'd had other plans, Lupe's father went to the marbles championship to _____.

   a. be with her brother   b. comfort her   c. encourage her

4. Lupe made friends with her first opponent because the girl was _____.

   a. alone   b. a champion   c. a terrible player

5. After Lupe won the marbles championship, the family went out for pizza in order to _____.

   a. forget what happened   b. cheer her brother   c. celebrate her win

Response to Literature Use with Student Edition page 165.

Have you ever been in a situation like the one Lupe faces? Draw a picture of a time when you felt the way Lupe did in the story.

Unit 3 • Reading 3   85

Grammar — Infinitives Use with Student Edition page 166.

REMEMBER An **infinitive** is formed with *to* + the base form of a verb. Infinitives can be used after certain verbs, such as *want* and *learn*. For verbs such as *allow* and *remind*, you must use an object after the verb and before the infinitive. Infinitives can also follow certain adjectives, such as *happy* and *afraid*.

Underline the infinitives in the following sentences. Then underline the verbs that precede the infinitives and circle the adjectives and objects.

Example: My mom <u>didn't allow</u> (us) <u>to go</u> to the party.

1. My cousin wants to play the drums in a band.
2. My friend reminded me to bring a jacket.
3. We decided to buy a new computer.
4. They hired my mom to send out emails about the charity.
5. I was sorry to leave early.

Complete the following sentences with the infinitive form of the verbs from the box.

| see | ~~be~~ | lose | meet | do | let |

Example: It appeared ____to be____ the end of the concert.

6. We were sorry _____ our game.
7. She was happy _____ me in her class.
8. They agreed _____ us at the mall.
9. My little brother refused _____ his homework.
10. I convinced my mother _____ me go on the camping trip.

Name _____ Date _____

Clarifying with Appositives and Colons *Use with Student Edition page 167.*

> **REMEMBER** An **appositive** is a noun or noun phrase that explains another noun. It is usually set off by commas. Sometimes, a **colon** and an appositive follow an independent clause. The clarification after the colon can be a phrase or a list. If the noun is singular or non-count, the appositive should be singular; if the noun is plural, the appositive should be plural.

Underline the appositive in each sentence. Then add commas to set off the appositives.

Example: Albert Einstein, <u>one of the greatest scientists ever</u>, was once told he had no good ideas.

1. Mr. Staunton the principal of the school will give a speech at graduation.
2. Kuala Lumpur the capital of Malaysia is a major trade center in Southeast Asia.
3. Simón Bolívar a famous nineteenth-century general led the fight for independence in many countries in South America.
4. Abraham Lincoln one of the great American presidents lost 23 out of 26 elections.

Add colons after the independent clauses to introduce the appositives.

Example: Sara had only one choice: to tell the teacher.

5. She gave me some good advice not to go there too early.
6. You have two choices for dinner chicken or fish.
7. Josef showed what a good son he was He made dinner for the family.
8. Sadira has only one thing on her mind to get rich.
9. I have lived in three countries Qatar, Kuwait, and Oman.
10. Shakespeare is a widely-read author His works have been translated into hundreds of languages.

Unit 3 • Reading 3

Writing — **Write a News Article** *Use with Student Edition pages 168–169.*

Complete your own 5Ws chart about a recent event.

Who?

↓

What?

↓

Where?

↓

When?

↓

Why?

Have your partner complete (✓) the Peer Review Checklist. Use this feedback to help you edit your final draft.

Peer Review Checklist

- ☐ Does the article focus on an interesting event?
- ☐ Does it answer the 5Ws?
- ☐ Does the writer show knowledge of the topic?
- ☐ Do sentences vary in length and pattern?
- ☐ Are appositives and infinitives used correctly?
- ☐ Could changes be made to improve the article?

Name _____ Date _____

Writing Workshop   *Use with Student Edition pages 174–177.*

Organize your ideas in the graphic organizer below.

Who?	
What?	
Where?	
When?	
Why?	

Have your partner complete (✓) the Peer Review Checklist. Use this feedback to help you edit your final draft.

Peer Review Checklist
- ☐ Does the article hold my interest?
- ☐ Does it answer all 5Ws?
- ☐ Are details presented in an order that makes sense?
- ☐ Does the writer choose words that fit the topic?
- ☐ Does the writer use adjectival clauses correctly?
- ☐ Could changes be made to improve the article?

Learning Log *Use after completing Student Edition page 178.*

Underline the vocabulary terms you know and can use well. Review and practice any you haven't underlined. Underline them when you know them well.

Literary Words	Key Words	Academic Words	
extended metaphor repetition stanza character motivation suspense	enterprise excelled famine satellite scholarships self-portrait	aid commitment global priority distinctive interpret precise pursue considerable	objective participate previous

Put a check by the skills you can perform well. Review and practice any you haven't checked off. Check them off when you can perform them well.

Skills	I can . . .
Word Study	☐ recognize and pronounce the prefixes *under-*, *re-*, *multi-*, *inter-*. ☐ recognize and use homophones. ☐ recognize and use the inflections *-ed* and *-ing*.
Reading Strategies	☐ connect ideas. ☐ identify author's purpose. ☐ predict.
Grammar	☐ use complex sentences with restrictive and nonrestrictive adjectival clauses. ☐ use gerunds as subjects or objects after verbs and prepositions. ☐ use infinitives and clarify with appositives and colons.
Writing	☐ write to compare and contrast. ☐ write about problems and solutions. ☐ write a news article. ☐ write an expository essay.

Name _____ Date _____

Test Preparation

Test 1

DIRECTIONS
Read this selection. Then answer the questions that follow it.

The Orange Show

1   In 1956, Jeff McKissack got permission to build a beauty salon. A beauty salon was a nice addition to the neighborhood. But what the neighbors got instead was something important to the whole state.

2   For the next 24 years, McKissack created a building that honored his favorite fruit: the orange. He filled the building with statues, murals, and more. He created everything from objects found around town. Bricks, fence posts, and farm tools became weird, beautiful art. The building became known as the Orange Show.

3   When McKissack died in 1980, people worked quickly to protect the Orange Show. The building was turned into a museum. The museum offered tours to visitors. Workers designed an Orangemobile. This inspired people to start a parade of nothing but Art Cars.

4   Today the Orange Show sends teachers to schools all over the city. The Art Car Parade is an annual event taking place each spring. The museum has brought artists to the city to paint murals. McKissack's love of the orange turned into a lot of beauty!

1 What is the purpose of the selection?
   A To inform the reader about an important place
   B To persuade the reader to visit the Orange Show
   C To encourage the reader to eat oranges
   D To tell Jeff McKissack's life story

2 In the selection, what does annual mean?
   A very old
   B every year
   C important
   D one time

Test 2

DIRECTIONS
Read this selection. Then answer the questions that follow it.

Run to the Finish

1   Max looked up into the stands and saw his mom and dad. He gave them a small wave. He raised his arms over his head into a long stretch. Then he bent over and checked the laces on his shoes. This was it. This was the moment he pictured every day when he woke up at 5:00 a.m. to train. The long hours of running, weight lifting, and practice had brought him here.

2   It was time for the race. He moved into his starting position. He closed his eyes and took a deep breath. TWEET! The starting whistle sounded.

3   Max ran faster then he ever had before. His feet pounded the track and sweat rolled into his eyes. He passed runner number five, then number seven, and finally number three. There was one runner left. Could he do it? Max's lungs and legs burned. He saw the finish line. The yellow ribbon snapped.

4   Max crossed the finish line in second place. He was overjoyed. Second place was great—his best finish ever! He looked up and saw his mom jumping up and down. He smiled at her and then walked over to congratulate the other runners.

1 What is Max doing in this story?
  A He is in a swimming race.
  B He is running a race.
  C He is skiing.
  D He is skateboarding.

2 Which sentence in paragraph 4 tells how Max feels about finishing in second place?
  A *He smiled at her and then walked over to congratulate the other runners.*
  B *Max crossed the finish line in second place.*
  C *He looked up and saw his mom jumping up and down.*
  D *He was overjoyed.*

3 Read this dictionary entry for the word train.

> **train** *v.* **1.** to direct the growth of a plant **2.** to teach a profession **3.** to get ready for a test of skill **4.** to aim at an object

Which definition of *train* is meant in paragraph 1?

  A Definition 1
  B Definition 2
  C Definition 3
  D Definition 4

4 According to the story, what did Max do to get ready for the race?
  A Eat healthy meals
  B Run for hours
  C Watch other racers
  D Run five miles

Test 3

DIRECTIONS
Read this selection. Then answer the questions that follow it.

John F. Kennedy and the Press

1   Throughout history, successful U.S. presidents have brought new ideas with them as they have taken the office of president. One of those successful presidents was John F. Kennedy.

2   During John F. Kennedy's presidency, televisions became popular throughout the United States. John F. Kennedy was the first U.S. president to put his press conferences on television. His successors, or the presidents who came after him, have continued this tradition.

3   Today, presidents use press conferences to tell their views of current events and issues. Presidents hope to shape public opinion by persuading the public to support their opinions. Presidents can begin with a statement and then take questions from the press. The press is the name for people who work for television stations, newspapers, and magazines. Presidents generally know what questions the press will probably ask, so they prepare responses before the conference.

4   Members of the press come to the press conference for a different reason. They are looking for a news story to share with people. The story is usually about something the president has done and why. The press uses the conference to ask the president to explain his or her decisions and plans to deal with certain issues. In this way, the press helps hold the president responsible for his or her actions. The job of the press is to inform the public by telling such stories.

5   Thanks to John F. Kennedy, people today can watch the president's press conferences and hear the president's views directly. They can also hear questions that the press uses to get explanations.

Test Preparation

1 Look at this graphic organizer about presidential press conferences.

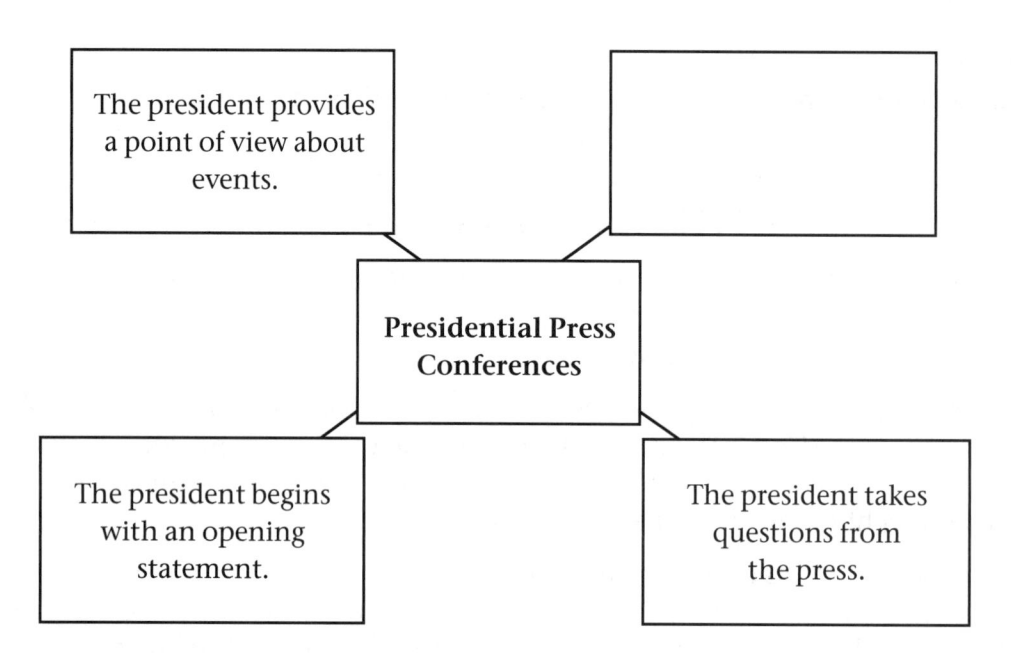

```
┌─────────────────┐                    ┌─────────────────┐
│ The president   │                    │                 │
│ provides a point│                    │                 │
│ of view about   │                    │                 │
│ events.         │                    │                 │
└────────┬────────┘                    └────────┬────────┘
         │      ┌─────────────────────┐         │
         └──────┤ Presidential Press  ├─────────┘
         ┌──────┤    Conferences      ├─────────┐
         │      └─────────────────────┘         │
┌────────┴────────┐                    ┌────────┴────────┐
│ The president   │                    │ The president   │
│ begins with an  │                    │ takes questions │
│ opening         │                    │ from the press. │
│ statement.      │                    │                 │
└─────────────────┘                    └─────────────────┘
```

1 Which of these statements belongs in the empty box?

   A Members of the press are looking for a story.
   B The press informs the public.
   C The president wants to persuade the public.
   D The press holds the president responsible.

2 In paragraph 2, what words help the reader know what <u>successors</u> means?

   A conferences on television
   B presidents who came after him
   C press conferences
   D continued this tradition

3 Paragraph 3 is mainly about —

   A why the press goes to a press conference
   B how to ask questions during a press conference
   C the president's purpose for holding a press conference
   D how the president answers the questions of the press

4 According to the article, why does the press attend the press conferences?

   A They want to tell their opinions.
   B They are looking for a news story.
   C They want to find out about current events.
   D They want to persuade Americans to support their opinions.

5 The purpose of the selection is to —

   A explain the purpose of presidential press conferences
   B describe how reporters write questions for press conferences
   C encourage people to watch press conferences
   D invite people to watch a press conference

Name _____ Date _____

Visual Literacy: Smithsonian American
Art Museum *Use with Student Edition pages 180–181.*

Learning to Look

Look at *Self-Portrait* by Malvina Hoffman on page 180 in your Student Edition. Use this artwork to complete the web diagram below. For each "string" coming from the center, list one observation about the artwork.

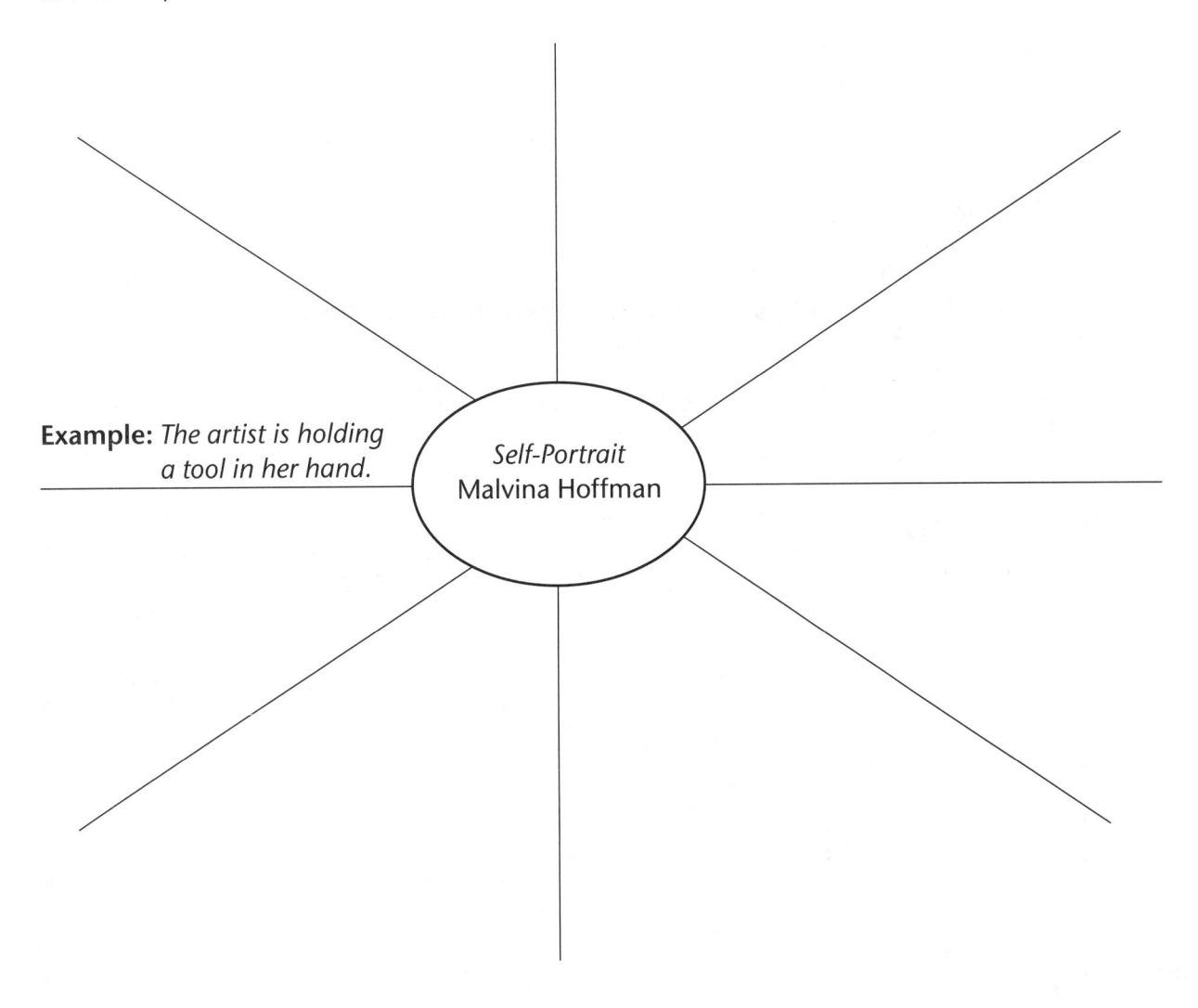

Example: *The artist is holding a tool in her hand.*

Self-Portrait
Malvina Hoffman

Unit 3 • Visual Literacy: Smithsonian American Art Museum   95

Interpretation

Look at *Self Portrait* by Chuck Close on page 181 in your Student Edition. Close combines many small painted squares to create a larger image. What other shapes do you see in this painting? List three of them below.

Example: *His eyeglasses are round.*

1. _____

2. _____

3. _____

KWLH

Look at *Self-Portrait* by Malvina Hoffman on page 180 of your Student Edition and *Self Portrait* by Chuck Close on page 181 of your Student Edition to complete the KWLH Chart below.

K	W	L	H
What do you **know** about self-portraits?	From their portraits, what do you **want** to learn about Hoffman or Close?	What have you **learned** about self-portraits?	**How** did you learn it?

Name _____ Date _____

UNIT 4: Can we see change as it happens?

Reading 1: "Changing Earth"

Vocabulary — Key Words *Use with Student Edition page 185.*

Write each word in the box next to its definition.

| fertilizers | fossil fuels | hybrid | microscopic | resources | solar power |

Example: _microscopic_: extremely small

1. _____: substances that are put on soil to make plants grow

2. _____: energy drawn from the sun

3. _____: something created by the slow decay of plants and animals over millions of years

4. _____: something found in a country that can be used to increase its wealth, such as oil, coal, or useful land

5. _____: something that is made from a mixture of two or more things

Use the words in the box at the top of the page to complete the sentences.

6. _____ are one of this country's most important natural _____.

7. The _____ will help the plants in the garden grow.

8. _____ cars use a mixture of gasoline and electricity.

9. The scientist looked at the _____ cells to study the disease.

10. When the sun is not shining, you can't use _____ to create electricity.

Vocabulary
Academic Words *Use with Student Edition page 186.*

Read the paragraph below. Pay attention to the underlined Academic Words.

> We need to find a way to reduce pollution. Earth's population is growing, and we need to make changes that will <u>accommodate</u> a greater number of people. We need to ask the government to pass another <u>regulation</u> to lower air pollution. We need to ask industries to find safe, clean <u>alternative</u> fuels and energy sources. Doing this will <u>enable</u> our children to live in a cleaner, safer environment.

Write Academic Words from the paragraph above next to their correct definitions.

Example: ___alternative___ : something you can use or do instead of something else

1. _____ : create room for something

2. _____ : make something possible

3. _____ : official rule or order

Use the Academic Words from the paragraph to complete the sentences.

4. It is a school _____ that there is no skateboarding on the property.

5. The huge stadium can _____ thousands of people.

6. The new building design will _____ people to use natural sunlight.

7. I find biking a fun and healthy _____ to driving.

Complete the sentences with your own ideas.

Example: I enjoy being able to accommodate guests when ___my cousins from Madiera visit___.

8. A good alternative to watching television is _____.

9. In our school, some of the best regulations are _____.

10. A new car would enable our family to _____.

Name _____ Date _____

Word Study Related Words *Use with Student Edition page 187.*

REMEMBER Some nouns and adjectives are related to the base form of the word. Knowing what the base form of the verb means can help you figure out related nouns and adjectives. For example, the verb *sense* is related to the noun *sensation* and the adjective *sensible*.

Look at the chart. Write the noun and adjective forms of the verbs. Write the noun and adjectives of the verbs on the chart.

Verb	Noun	Adjective
Example: produce	+ -ion = production	+ -ed = produced
1. collect	+ -ion =	+ -ed =
2. create	+ -ion =	+ -ed =
3. digest	+ -ion =	+ -ed =
4. medicate	+ -ion =	+ -ed =
5. migrate	+ -ion =	+ -ed =

Create the noun form of the verbs. Check a dictionary if needed. Then use the new nouns in sentences.

Example: act + -ion =
 action   The movie has a lot of action.

6. celebrate
 _____

7. decorate
 _____

8. participate
 _____

9. demonstrate
 _____

10. educate
 _____

Unit 4 • Reading 1

Reading Strategy: Skim and Scan

Use with Student Edition page 187.

REMEMBER When you **skim** a text, you read quickly without stopping. When you **scan** something, look for particular things that you want to know. For example, look for dates, numbers, ideas, names, and other types of information. Look at the title and visuals, and move your eyes quickly over the words. Stop scanning when you see the key words you need.

Skim and scan the paragraphs. Look for information about what James has done to help his school become more environmentally friendly. List three things he did.

> James felt that he wanted to do more to help the environment. Many people drive cars in Los Angeles, and he often saw smog, a type of pollution, in the air. He tried to convince his parents that they should buy a hybrid car, which uses less gasoline. His family could not afford a new car, but they all decided that they should drive their car less. They agreed not to use the car on weekends and to use public transportation, walk, or bike instead.
>
> James still wanted to do more. He read about environmental issues and decided to write a letter to the editor of his town newspaper. He asked if his city could use solar or wind power to generate electricity. The newspaper published his letter. A reporter also interviewed him about the work he had done to help the environment.
>
> James gave a presentation to his class at school. He told them about the things they could do every day to improve the environment. Some of James's classmates suggested starting a recycling program at school, and he helped them. James and his classmates raised enough money to help their school install solar panels and use solar energy.

1. _____
2. _____
3. _____

4. Scan the paragraphs. Describe the agreement that James's family made to be more environmentally friendly.
   _____
   _____

5. Scan the paragraphs. What did James do to try to convince the city to be more environmentally friendly? Write your answer below.
   _____
   _____

Name _____ Date _____

Comprehension Use with Student Edition page 194.

Choose the best answer for each item. Circle the letter of the correct answer.

1. Over the past 200 years, Earth has changed very _____.

   a. quickly b. slowly c. easily

2. Scientists have been working to find new ways to increase the _____.

   a. pollution b. food supply c. animal population

3. Fossil fuels are nonrenewable sources of _____.

   a. food b. plants c. energy

4. Hybrid cars preserve natural resources by using both gasoline and _____.

   a. electricity b. water c. solar power

5. Three alternative sources of energy are _____.

   a. nuclear, solar, and wind
   b. nuclear, water, and coal
   c. solar, wind, and coal

Extension Use with Student Edition page 195.

In the chart below, list five things you can do to help conserve natural resources. In the second column, write the name of the natural resource that each action would help to conserve.

What I Can Do to Help	Natural Resource
use less paper	trees

Unit 4 • Reading 1

Grammar: Present Perfect *Use with Student Edition page 196.*

REMEMBER Use the **present perfect** to talk about actions that happened at an unspecified time in the past. Form the present perfect with *have* or *has* + the past participle. Form regular past participles by adding *-d* or *-ed* to the base form of the verb. Irregular past participles include *be / been*, *give / given*, and *do / done*. The contraction of *have* is *'ve* and *has* is *'s*. Form the negative with *have not* (*haven't*) and *has not* (*hasn't*). *Have* or *has* comes at the beginning of questions. Use *already* to talk about a past event that happened sooner than expected and *yet* to talk about an event that hasn't happened up to now.

Complete the chart with the present perfect forms of the verbs. Use a dictionary if necessary.

Base Form	Present Perfect
Example: go	has/have gone
1. be	
2. grow	
3. have	
4. find	
5. use	

Complete the sentences with the verbs in parentheses. Write the verbs in the present perfect. Make sure that the subjects and the verbs agree in number.

6. (grow) The population of our city _____ in the last fifty years.

7. (change) Scientists' opinions _____ over the years.

8. (become) Programs for recycling _____ more popular.

Write sentences with the present perfect form of the verb in parentheses and *already* or *yet*.

9. (come / already) (the mail)

_____

10. (eat / yet) (we)

_____

102   Unit 4 • Reading 1

Name _____ Date _____

Conjunctive Adverbs *Use with Student Edition page 197.*

> **REMEMBER** A **conjunctive adverb** is one word and an **adverbial phrase** is more than one word. They both function as adverbs and help you transition from one idea to another. They can be used to show contrast (*however, nevertheless, at the same time*); show result (*therefore, thus, consequently, as a result*); show addition (*furthermore, indeed*); and show comparison (*similarly*). Conjunctive adverbs and adverbial phrases are followed by commas and always begin a sentence or an independent clause. Use a semicolon between two independent clauses.

Circle the correct conjunctive adverb or adverbial phrase in the following pairs of sentences. Then rewrite the sentences as one, using semicolons.

Example: He was sleepy. ((As a result)/ However), he went to bed early.
   He was sleepy; as a result, he went to bed early.

1. Jack enjoys watching basketball. (At the same time / Indeed), he doesn't play.
   _____

2. Saul is a good student. (However / Indeed), he always gets the highest grades.
   _____

3. I'd like to get a dog. (However / Consequently), I don't have time to take care of it.
   _____

4. Brett isn't going to Spain. (Therefore / Nevertheless), he's studying Spanish.
   _____

5. My mom said I could go tonight. (Furthermore / Thus), I can stay out till 11:00.
   _____

Unit 4 • Reading 1   103

Writing **Write an Advertisement** *Use with Student Edition pages 198–199.*

Complete your own graphic organizer for an advertisement that will persuade people to buy something that is good for the environment. Include your opinion, a reason, and examples.

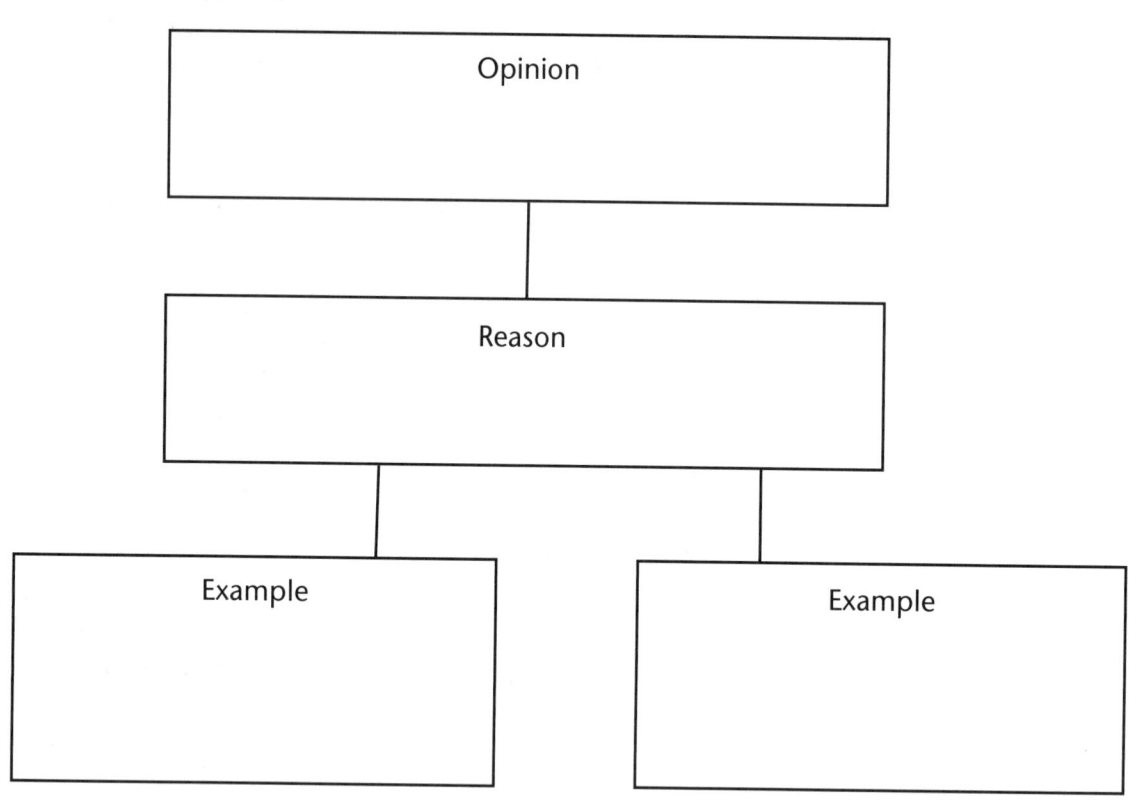

```
          ┌─────────────────┐
          │     Opinion     │
          └────────┬────────┘
                   │
          ┌────────┴────────┐
          │     Reason      │
          └────────┬────────┘
           ┌───────┴───────┐
   ┌───────┴──────┐ ┌──────┴───────┐
   │   Example    │ │   Example    │
   └──────────────┘ └──────────────┘
```

Have your partner complete (✓) the Peer Review Checklist. Use this feedback to help you edit your final draft.

Peer Review Checklist

☐ Does the ad focus on a product friendly to the environment?
☐ Does the ad support opinions with reasons and examples?
☐ Does the ad use persuasive words to appeal to the audience?
☐ Are new vocabulary words used accurately?
☐ Are the present perfect and conjunctive adverbs used correctly?
☐ Could changes be made to improve the ad?

Name _____ Date _____

UNIT 4: Can we see change as it happens?

Reading 2: from *Through My Eyes*

Vocabulary — Key Words *Use with Student Edition page 201.*

Write each word in the box next to its definition.

| civil rights | federal court | justices | racism | segregation | troops |

Example: __civil rights__: rights, such as the right to vote or the right to be treated fairly by the law, that every person should have, whatever his or her sex, race, or religion

1. _____: place where the laws of the Constitution and the national government of the United States are upheld

2. _____: judges in the supreme court for a country or state

3. _____: a group of soldiers

4. _____: the belief that different races of people have different characteristics and abilities, and that one race is better than others

5. _____: the practice of keeping people of different races, sexes, or religions apart, and making them live, work, and go to school separately

Use the words in the box at the top of the page to complete the sentences.

6. In our history, people have worked hard to win their _____.

7. The _____ of the U.S. Supreme Court make decisions about federal laws.

8. When _____ was legal, children of different races were not allowed to swim in the same swimming pool.

9. Military _____ are sent to fight wars.

10. Nobody should ever tolerate _____.

Vocabulary — **Academic Words** *Use with Student Edition page 202.*

Read the paragraph. Pay attention to the underlined Academic Words.

> In the past, African Americans were treated unfairly. Many schools and other places in the South were segregated, and people refused to <u>integrate</u> them. It was <u>apparent</u> to Dr. Martin Luther King, Jr. that this situation had to change. Dr. King decided to <u>undertake</u> a movement for equality. Through peaceful protests and inspiring speeches, he taught people to work together to change the laws. Dr. Martin Luther King, Jr. became a hero and a <u>symbol</u> of the civil rights movement.

Write Academic Words from the paragraph next to their correct definitions.

Example: __undertake__: start to do something

1. _____: easy to understand; obvious

2. _____: a picture, a letter, or a sign that means or stands for something else

3. _____: unite; end the practice of separating people of different races

Use the Academic Words from the paragraph to complete the sentences.

4. I am about to _____ a big project.

5. It was _____ that Ramesh was the tallest boy in the class.

6. She likes to _____ hip-hop and ballet in her dancing.

7. The stop sign is an easy _____ to recognize.

Complete the sentences with your own ideas.

Example: In my school, it is apparent that __the students work very hard__.

8. One thing I would like to undertake is _____.

9. The Smiley Face is a symbol of _____.

10. It was important to integrate schools because _____.

106   Unit 4 • Reading 2

Name _____ Date _____

Word Study — **Capitalizing Proper Nouns** *Use with Student Edition page 203.*

REMEMBER A **proper noun** names a specific person, place, or thing. It must be capitalized. For example: Abraham Lincoln, Nevada, Bill of Rights.

Look at the chart. Capitalize the proper nouns. Write them in the chart.

Incorrect Proper Noun	Capitalized Proper Noun
Example: pluto	Pluto
1. empire state building	
2. george Washington	
3. spanish	
4. american revolution	
5. golden gate bridge	

Correct the sentences by capitalizing the proper nouns. Write the correct sentences on the lines.

Example: lee is chinese

Lee is Chinese.

6. dr. green lives on main street.

_____

7. Tomorrow luz visits yellowstone national park.

_____

8. On friday, greg takes a french test.

_____

9. plainview high school closes in june.

_____

10. mr. cole talked about venus and jupiter.

_____

Unit 4 • Reading 2

Reading Strategy: Draw Conclusions

Use with Student Edition page 203.

> **REMEMBER** When you **draw conclusions**, you try to figure out the meanings of clues and events in a text. Think about what you already know and whether the information you have makes sense.

Read the paragraphs and underline the clues that you can use to draw conclusions about what is happening. Then answer each question.

1. Lucas walked slowly into the building. His hands were shaking. He quickly put his hands in his pockets. Lucas didn't want his new classmates to know how he was feeling.

    What conclusion can you draw about Lucas?

    _____

2. The kids were different from Lucas. They wore different clothes. Their parents drove different cars. They seemed to have everything they wanted.

    What conclusion can you draw about Lucas?

    _____

3. A boy came up to Lucas in the hall. The boy was bigger and taller than Lucas. Lucas stood up straight and looked the boy in the eyes. He wanted to seem brave. "It's my first day here," the boy said. Lucas relaxed and smiled.

    What conclusion can you draw about the boy?

    _____

4. "It's my first day, too," Lucas said. "I'm Lucas."
    "I'm Russ," the boy said. "Did your parents just move into the neighborhood?"
    "Actually, I'm living with my aunt and uncle," Lucas said.

    What conclusion can you draw about Lucas?

    _____

5. A group of kids walked by Lucas and Russ.
    "Nice shirt," one kid said sarcastically. All the kids laughed. Lucas felt his face get hot. "Don't worry about them," Russ said. Lucas looked up at Russ and smiled. Together, they walked down the hall to their first class.

    What conclusion can you draw about Russ and Lucas?

    _____

Name _____ Date _____

Comprehension   Use with Student Edition page 210.

Choose the best answer for each item. Circle the letter of the correct answer.

1. In 1954, the Supreme Court ordered _____.

   a. the beginning of separate schools for blacks and whites
   b. the end of racism in the United States
   c. the end of "separate but equal" education

2. To get into a white school, black kindergartners had to _____.

   a. wait in line
   b. pass a test
   c. walk very far

3. Ruby's father didn't want her to go to a white school because he was worried _____.

   a. she would miss her friends at her old school
   b. she would have to walk too far
   c. she would not be treated as an equal

4. Ruby was taken to school on the first day by _____.

   a. her mother and father
   b. her mother and federal marshals
   c. her mother and a member of the NAACP

5. When Ruby walked into her new school _____.

   a. people yelled and threw things
   b. people cheered and clapped
   c. the other students laughed at her

Extension   Use with Student Edition page 211.

Write a short answer to the question.

What do you think it was like to be a teenager in the southern United States before the civil rights movement? Write a paragraph that compares and contrasts the experiences of black teenagers and white teenagers at that time and place.

_____
_____
_____
_____
_____

Unit 4 • Reading 2

Grammar — Compound and Complex Sentences

Use with Student Edition page 212.

REMEMBER A **coordinating conjunction** can connect two independent clauses to make a compound sentence. *And*, *but*, and *so* are coordinating conjunctions. *And* connects two similar ideas; *but* contrasts two ideas; and *so* connects a cause and result. A **subordinating conjunction** can connect an independent clause and one or more dependent clauses. *Because* and *since* are subordinating conjunctions.

Complete the sentences with *and*, *but*, or *so* to make compound sentences.

Example: We all ate our breakfast, ____*and*____ then we went to school.

1. James got the highest score on the test, _____ he received an award.

2. My dog's not very smart, _____ he's very affectionate.

3. Bring me my wallet, _____ I'll give you some money.

4. It was a beautiful day, _____ we went hiking.

Match the independent clauses on the left to the dependent clauses on the right to form complex sentences.

Example: He jumped off the platform	since I had a new computer.
5. I asked for a video game	since Ricardo had to go home.
6. The game is over	because they had some new books.
7. I went to the library	because it was his turn to dive.

Use your own words to complete the compound or complex sentences.

Example: Please bring me a sandwich, and ____*bring me some ketchup*____.

8. Because I worked so hard, _____.

9. Since she left early, _____.

10. We reached the train just in time, but _____.

Name _____ Date _____

Agreement in Compound and Complex Sentences
Use with Student Edition page 213.

> **REMEMBER** Compound and complex sentences may have pronouns and antecedents or subjects and verbs that are separated by words. When you write these sentences, be sure these words agree; that is, the pronoun and antecedent should match (*Emily/her, the players/they*, etc.), and the subject and verb should both be either singular or plural (*Xavier skates, Mauro and Jess sing*).

Underline the antecedent in each sentence. Then write the correct pronoun.

Example: <u>Stella</u> wasn't in class, so _____she_____ missed the test.

1. Since the children just ate lunch, _____ won't be hungry.

2. Because Aunt Cara likes to garden, I gave _____ a rosebush.

3. Jim couldn't call me since _____ lost his phone.

4. My brother and I can play basketball, but _____ can't play football.

5. Anne talks a lot since _____ is nervous.

Underline the subject in each sentence. Then write the correct form of the verb in parentheses.

Example: <u>Mrs. Gomez</u> gets confused sometimes, so she (ask) _____asks_____ me for help.

6. Ruby's parents disagree, but they (allow) _____ her to go to the new school.

7. The town has plenty of activities, so it (be) _____ fun to visit.

8. I want to see the movie because I (need) _____ a break from studying.

9. Since Jared has the tools, he (be going to help) _____ me fix my bike.

10. Because Ruby's mother is nervous, she (worry) _____ about Ruby in school.

Unit 4 • Reading 2

Writing — Write a Persuasive Paragraph

Use with Student Edition pages 214–215.

Complete your own graphic organizer for a persuasive paragraph about a situation, rule, or law you believe is unfair. Use a question-and-answer format, and include reasons.

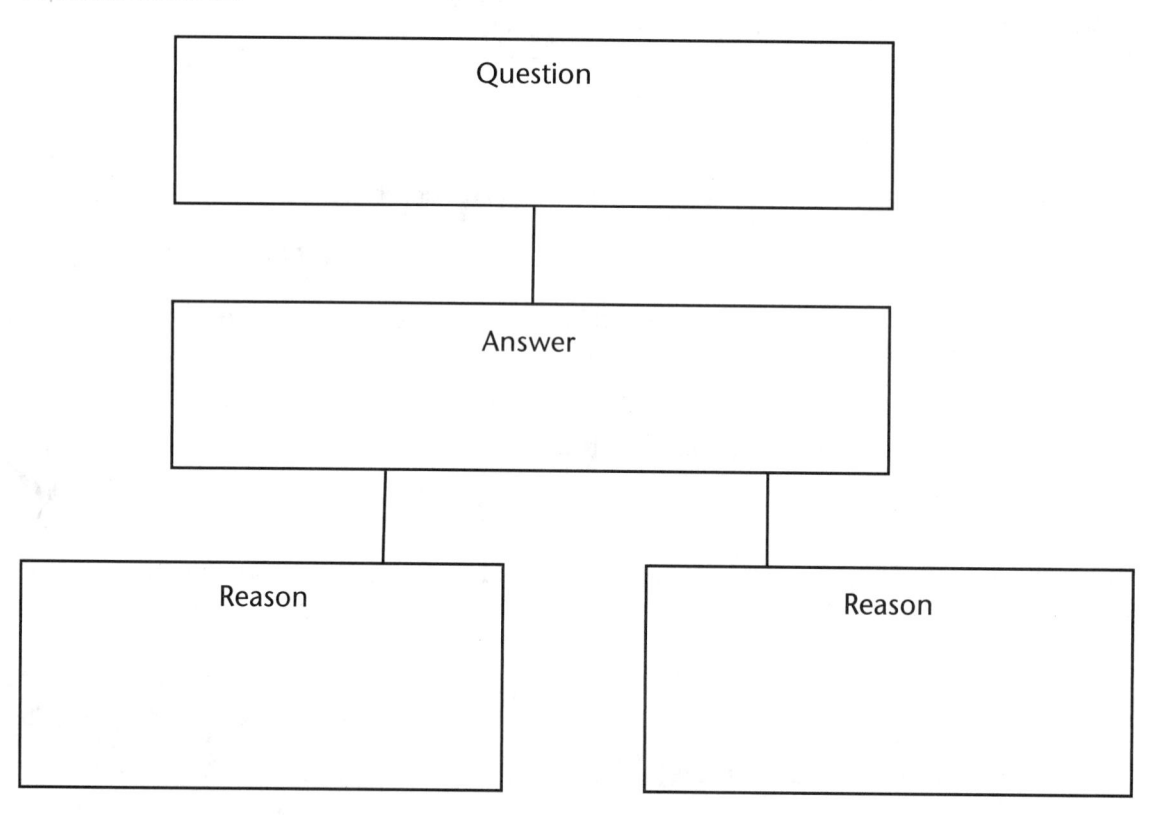

```
┌─────────────────────────┐
│        Question         │
└────────────┬────────────┘
             │
┌────────────┴────────────┐
│         Answer          │
└──────┬───────────┬──────┘
       │           │
┌──────┴────┐ ┌────┴──────┐
│  Reason   │ │  Reason   │
└───────────┘ └───────────┘
```

Have your partner complete (✓) the Peer Review Checklist. Use this feedback to help you edit your final draft.

Peer Review Checklist

- ☐ Does the paragraph ask a question and answer it persuasively?
- ☐ Does the writer state a clear opinion?
- ☐ Is the writer's opinion supported by good reasons?
- ☐ Do persuasive words appeal to readers' emotions?
- ☐ Do sentences vary in length and pattern?
- ☐ Could changes be made to improve the paragraph?

Name _____ Date _____

UNIT 4: Can we see change as it happens?

Reading 3: from *Anne of Green Gables*

Vocabulary — **Literary Words** *Use with Student Edition page 217.*

> **REMEMBER** **Conflict** is a disagreement or struggle between two or more people or forces.
> **Foreshadowing** is a hint in a story that something else is going to happen later on.

Read the sentences below. Describe who has the conflict and what it is about, and then write a possible solution.

Example: Amy has only two dollars, and her friends want to go out for pizza.
Conflict: *Amy doesn't have enough money to pay for her pizza*.
Possible solution: *Amy could borrow money from one of her friends*.

1. When Margot got home with her new sweater, she realized it had a hole in it. She couldn't find her receipt. The salesperson at the store doesn't remember Margot.

   Conflict: _____

   Possible solution: _____

2. Fran expected Raj to bring her some flowers when she had the flu. However, he never even called. Raj said he didn't know Fran was sick.

   Conflict: _____

   Possible solution: _____

Write what the sentences below might foreshadow.

Example: Just as the fireworks started, a black cloud appeared over the crowd.
Foreshadowed event: *The rain began, and everyone got wet*.

3. Merci handed her phone to her sister. "Here, hold this for me while I go swimming. And please be careful not to delete any photos. I only have one picture of Luca."

   Foreshadowed event: _____

4. Julio read the instructions from his neighbor one more time: "Take the dog for a walk before you put the kids to bed. The twins can ride in the stroller, but they are scared of going too fast. Please walk slowly." Julio tied the dog's leash to the stroller as he put the note in his pocket. Just then, a squirrel ran by.

   Foreshadowed event: _____

Unit 4 • Reading 3

Vocabulary — Academic Words
Use with Student Edition page 218.

Read the paragraph. Pay attention to the underlined Academic Words.

> The early 1900s was a difficult <u>period</u> for many young children. Due to many <u>circumstances</u> beyond their control, parents often could not afford to keep their children and had to send them to an orphanage. Sometimes farmers needed help, so they would adopt a child to help them <u>labor</u> in the field. While many girls were capable of hard work, people assumed boys were the best <u>gender</u> for doing work.

Match each word with its definition.

Example: __b__ labor   **a.** situations

_____ 1. gender   **b.** hard physical work

_____ 2. period   **c.** male or female

_____ 3. circumstances   **d.** a specific time

Use the Academic Words from the exercise above to complete the sentences.

4. Many people feel that certain colors are associated with a particular _____, like pink for girls and blue for boys.

5. My friend's parents expect him to do a lot of _____ around the house during the summer.

6. There was a _____ when Picasso painted only blue paintings for a long time.

7. The _____ surrounding the missing diamond necklace suggested that it had been stolen.

Complete the sentences with your own ideas.

Example: If I could change any circumstances in my friend's life, I would __make his house much closer to mine__.

8. The most exciting period in music was _____.

9. The gender I prefer to babysit is _____.

10. One type of labor I enjoy doing is _____.

Name _____ Date _____

Word Study — Spelling Long e *Use with Student Edition page 219.*

REMEMBER Words with the **long e** sound can be spelled *ee*, *ea*, *e*, and *y*.

Read the words in the box. Then write the words in the correct column in the chart.

| bean | beet | be | busy | sunny | east | steam | she | steel | tiny | feel | we |

ee	ea
beet	

e	y

Write sentences with four of the words, using each spelling shown below.

1. (ee) _____
2. (ea) _____
3. (e) _____
4. (y) _____

Unit 4 • Reading 3

Reading Strategy | **Summarize**

Use with Student Edition page 219.

> **REMEMBER** Summarizing the events that lead to a change in a character will help you understand and remember what you read. Try to answer the basic questions in your summary: *who, what, when, where, why, how.*

Read the following paragraphs. Then answer *who, what, when, where, why,* **and** *how.*

> Matthew and Marilla Cuthbert lived a quiet life on Prince Edward Island. They were siblings, but neither of them married, so they lived in the same home they had grown up in: Green Gables. One day they realized they were getting older and could use some help around the farm. Marilla had heard about one of her neighbors adopting a young boy to do some physical labor. Matthew agreed that it was a good idea to do the same thing; it was the early 1900s, and many children needed homes where they could be comfortable and have enough to eat. Unfortunately, when Matthew went to pick up the boy, the person waiting for him was Anne—a girl.

1. Who _____
   What _____
   When _____
   Where _____
   Why _____
   How _____

> Anne Shirley was a bright and talkative girl with red hair and freckles. When Matthew came to pick her up at the train station, she was excited. She had heard of their town and its beautiful fields and orchards. Along the way, she chatted to Matthew about everything she saw. Matthew was extremely shy and was reluctant to tell Anne that there had been a mistake. As he listened to her talk, though, he found that he was charmed by her bubbly and intelligent personality. He began to think that it would be a terrible thing to crush this girl's spirit by telling her she had to go back to the orphanage.

2. Who _____
   What _____
   When _____
   Where _____
   Why _____
   How _____

Name _____ Date _____

Comprehension Use with Student Edition page 226.

Choose the best answer for each item. Circle the letter of the correct answer.

1. The Cuthberts want to adopt a boy so they can have help with _____.

   a. cooking   b. driving   c. farming

2. The author describes Anne as having clothes that are _____.

   a. brightly colored   b. cheap and ill-fitting   c. clean and beautiful

3. Anne tells Matthew that on the train, Mrs. Spencer found Anne's questions to be _____.

   a. irritating   b. delightful   c. mysterious

4. Matthew decides that the best person to tell Anne about the mix-up will be _____.

   a. himself   b. Mrs. Spencer   c. Marilla

5. When Marilla meets Anne, she is surprised because Anne is _____.

   a. thin   b. red-headed   c. a girl

Response to Literature Use with Student Edition page 227.

After reading the excerpt from *Anne of Green Gables*, fill in the spaces in the chart.

What Matthew expected	How Matthew felt about girls and women	How Matthew reacted when he first met Anne	How Anne behaved on the ride home	How Matthew felt about Anne after spending time with her

Unit 4 • Reading 3   117

Grammar: Possessive Nouns and Adjectives

Use with Student Edition page 228.

> **REMEMBER** Possessive nouns show ownership. Form a possessive noun by adding '*s* to the noun. When a proper noun ends in *s*, such as *Mr. Hass*, add '*s*. However, when a common noun ends in *s*, such as the plural noun *students*, just add an apostrophe ('). The possessive pronouns *my, your, his, her, its, our,* and *they* function as adjectives and are always followed by nouns. Don't confuse them with the possessive pronouns *mine, yours, his, hers, its, ours,* and *theirs*, which replace the possessive noun phrase.

Add '*s* or an apostrophe to make the underlined noun possessive.

Example: I like <u>Virginia</u>'s new haircut.

1. <u>Our teachers</u> _____ offices are at the end of the hall.
2. <u>The restaurant</u> _____ alarm system wasn't working.
3. Have you met <u>Dr. Roberts</u> _____ wife?
4. I love <u>that house</u> _____ garden.
5. <u>The boxes</u> _____ seals were broken.

Complete the sentences with the correct possessive pronoun (*my, your, his, her, its, our,* or *they*).

Example: Marian gave me a book, but I don't remember _____its_____ title.

6. Tim borrowed my cell phone because _____ phone wasn't working.
7. Chris fell off a horse and broke _____ leg.
8. Children should obey _____ parents.
9. The cat is eating _____ food.
10. They have _____ reasons for not coming.

Name _____ Date _____

Antecedent-Pronoun and Subject-Verb Agreement
Use with Student Edition page 229.

> **REMEMBER** An **antecedent** is what comes before the pronouns that refer to it in a sentence or series of sentences. Pronouns must agree with their antecedent, and verbs must agree with the nouns or pronouns they are used with.

Underline the antecedent in each sentence. Then circle all the pronouns that refer to it.

Example: <u>Susan</u> turned the TV on after (she)'d finished washing (her) hair.

1. Mary wondered whether she should bring her cell phone to the meeting.
2. Dave thought that his new coat looked good on him.
3. When the officers stopped me, they got out of their car.
4. When did your sister get her ears pierced?
5. The team was late, but they finally showed up.

Complete each sentence by circling the correct phrase that refers to the underlined antecedent.

Example: I can't find <u>the books</u>. I know (I was / (they were)) on the table.

6. Judy has <u>a grand piano</u>. (It costs / She costs) $3,000.
7. <u>Judy</u> has a grand piano. (It plays / She plays) it every day.
8. <u>Those apples</u> look delicious. (It is / They are) locally grown.
9. We saw <u>some kittens</u> in the backyard. (It was / They were) really cute.
10. We saw some kittens <u>in the backyard</u>. (It was / They were) really overgrown.

Unit 4 • Reading 3   119

Writing — Write a Review *Use with Student Edition pages 230–231.*

Complete your own graphic organizer about a book that you have read.

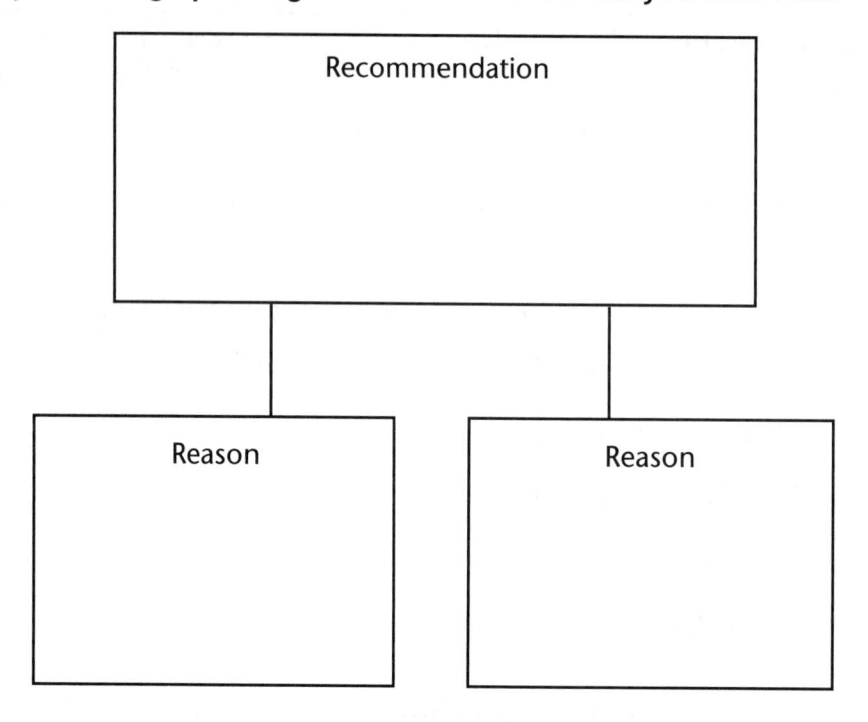

```
┌─────────────────────────────┐
│       Recommendation        │
│                             │
└──────────────┬──────────────┘
        ┌─────┴─────┐
┌───────┴───┐   ┌───┴───────┐
│  Reason   │   │  Reason   │
│           │   │           │
└───────────┘   └───────────┘
```

Have your partner complete (✓) the Peer Review Checklist. Use this feedback to help you edit your final draft.

Peer Review Checklist

- ☐ Does the review state an opinion about a book?
- ☐ Does it give reasons and examples in a logical order?
- ☐ Does the writing voice show the writer's feelings?
- ☐ Are verbs, tenses, and pronoun/antecedents used correctly?
- ☐ Is the possessive case used correctly?
- ☐ Could changes be made to improve the review?

Name _____ Date _____

Writing Workshop
Use with Student Edition pages 236–239.

Organize your ideas in the graphic organizer below.

For	Against

Have your partner complete (✓) the Peer Review Checklist. Use this feedback to help you edit your final draft.

Peer Review Checklist
- ☐ Did the essay sustain my interest?
- ☐ Did it persuade me to agree with the writer's opinion?
- ☐ Was the information easy for me to follow?
- ☐ Was the writer's voice enthusiastic and persuasive?
- ☐ Did the writer use the possessive case correctly?
- ☐ Could changes be made to improve the essay?

Learning Log *Use after completing Student Edition page 240.*

Underline the vocabulary items you know and can use well. Review and practice any you haven't underlined. Underline them when you know them well.

Literary Words	Key Words	Academic Words	
conflict foreshadowing	fertilizers fossil fuels hybrid microscopic resources solar power civil rights federal court justices racism segregation troops	accommodate alternative enable regulation apparent	integrate symbol undertake circumstances gender labor period

Put a check by the skills you can perform well. Review and practice any you haven't checked off. Check them off when you can perform them well.

Skills	I can . . .
Word Study	☐ recognize and use related words. ☐ capitalize proper nouns. ☐ recognize and spell words with the long *e*.
Reading Strategies	☐ skim and scan. ☐ draw conclusions. ☐ summarize.
Grammar	☐ use the present perfect correctly. ☐ use conjunctive adverbs. ☐ use compound and complex sentences with correct agreement. ☐ use possessive nouns and adjectives and recognize antecedent-pronoun and subject-verb agreement.
Writing	☐ write an advertisement. ☐ write a persuasive paragraph. ☐ write a review. ☐ write a persuasive essay.

Name _____ Date _____

Test Preparation

Test 1

DIRECTIONS
Read this selection. Then answer the questions that follow it.

Home

(1) Spike is a medium-sized dog. (2) He has had a hard life. (3) For several months, he lived on the street. (4) His only food was what he found in trashcans.

(5) Truman met Spike when he almost hit him as he was running across a parking lot. (6) Truman hit the brakes just in time. (7) He got out of his car to check on the dog. (8) Spike was scared, but fine.

(9) Truman put Spike in the car. (10) Spike sat on the seat and shook. (11) He had never been in a car. (12) Truman drove him to a shelter.

(13) At the shelter, Spike learned manners and a few tricks. (14) Finally, Spike got to visit people. (15) Jessie came to the shelter. (16) She, loved Spike right away. (17) Jessie took Spike to live at her house. (18) Now Spike knows what home really is.

1. What revision, if any, should be made in sentence 5?
   A Truman met Spike when he almost hit him. Spike was running across the parking lot.
   B Truman met Spike when Truman almost hit Spike as Spike was running across the parking lot.
   C Truman met Spike when he was running across the parking lot.
   D No revision is needed.

2. What change if any, should be made in sentence 16?
   A Change *loved* to *loves*
   B Change *away* to *now*
   C Delete the comma
   D Change *She* to *Jessie*

Test Preparation

Test 2

DIRECTIONS
Read this selection. Then answer the questions that follow it.

Ella wrote this paper for a class assignment. Ella would like you to read her rough draft and suggest corrections and improvements she should make.

Old Ollie

(1) Ollie is an old dog. (2) He has changed as he has grown older. (3) He used to be all black, and now he has white hair on his nose and chin. (4) He has white in his eyebrows, too.

(5) We got Ollie on a Sunday morning when he was about five months old. (6) My brother and I played with him all weekend?

(7) The next day we had to leave the house. (8) We took everything out of the bathroom that could possibly hurt Ollie. (9) We left him in there with some dog toys and his bed.

(10) After what happened in the bathroom, we didn't try to leave Ollie in any one special place. (11) He could go anywhere in the house. (12) He tried to be good. (13) He was scared when he was left alone. (14) He just wanted to be with us.

---

1 What change, if any, should be made to sentence 3?
   A Change *and* to *but*
   B Remove the comma
   C Change *has* to *had*
   D Make no change

2 What revision should be made to sentence 6?
   A Change *played* to *playing*
   B Change *I* to *me*
   C Change the question mark to a period
   D Change *him* to *her*

3 Which sentence could BEST follow and support sentence 9?
   A We found Ollie sleeping when we came home.
   B Ollie chewed his bed until the insides came out.
   C Ollie played with his toy, but he didn't sleep in his bed.
   D Ollie played with his toys and took a nap in his bed.

4 What is the BEST way to combine sentences 12 and 13?
   A He tried to be good, and he was scared when he was left alone.
   B He tried to be good; but he was scared when was left alone.
   C He was scared when he was left alone; and he tried to be good.
   D He tried to be good, but he was scared when he was left alone.

Test 3

DIRECTIONS
Read this selection. Then answer the questions that follow it.

Mark wrote this paper for his science class. Mark would like you to read his rough draft and suggest corrections and improvements he should make.

The Amazing Little Gopher

(1) Gophers dig holes in lawns and gardens. (2) However, they might think differently if they knew how amazing these small animals are.

(3) A gophers body is good for digging. (4) Gophers create their own underground homes by digging with their claws and teeth. (5) Digging uses a lot of energy, so gophers need a lot of food. (6) When they dig, they find roots. (7) They eat some of the roots, and they carry the rest to storage places. (8) They carry their food in pockets in their mouths.

(9) There isn't much room underground. (10) Gophers make up for that. (11) They are able to turn around in their tunnels because their bodies are made with special spines and loose skin. (12) When gophers to turn around, they push the dirt out of their way.

(13) When gophers dig their underground homes they leeve behind hills of dirt. (14) Some people may see the dirt, and think gophers are pests. (15) But if you think about how interesting they are, you may appreciate the way that gophers are prepared for the life they have.

1 Which sentence could BEST follow and support sentence 1?
   A Most gardeners do not like how gophers change their gardens.
   B Gophers can dig up to five holes each day.
   C Some gardeners like the changes gophers make in their lawn.
   D Gardeners work very hard to keep their grass green and the flowers growing.

2 What change, if any, should be made in sentence 3?
   A Change *digging* to **digged**
   B Change *is* to **are**
   C Change *gophers* to **gopher's**
   D Make no change

Test Preparation

125

3 What is the BEST way to combine sentences 9 and 10?

  A There isn't much room underground, and gophers make up for that.

  B There isn't much room underground; gophers make up for that.

  C There isn't much room underground, but gophers make up for that.

  D There isn't much room underground but gophers make up for that.

4 What revision, if any, should be made in sentence 12?

  A Remove the comma
  B Change *to turn* to **turn**
  C Change *push* to **pushed**
  D Make no revision

5 What change should be made in sentence 13?

  A Add a comma
  B Change *their* to **there**
  C Change *dig* to **will dig**
  D Change *leeve* to **leave**

6 What change, if any, should be made in sentence 14?

  A Remove the comma
  B Change *are* to **is**
  C Change *think* to **is thinking**
  D Change *and* to **so**

Name _____ Date _____

Visual Literacy: Smithsonian American Art Museum *Use with Student Edition pages 242–243.*

Learning to Look

Look at *Double Portrait of the Artist in Time* by Helen Lundeberg on page 243 in your Student Edition. Describe four things you see. State facts, not opinions.

Example: _Both the young girl at the table and the woman in the painting are holding flowers._

1. _____
2. _____
3. _____
4. _____

Interpretation

Look at *Double Portrait of the Artist in Time* again. Pick one object from the painting such as a flower. How did it get in the room? Who owns it? What is it doing there? Write your answers below.

Example: _An adult gave the child a flower to hold so she would look cute for the painting._

_____
_____
_____
_____

5W&H

Look at *Woman Lifting a Basket, Waving a Handkerchief,* from the book *Animal Locomotion* by Eadweard Muybridge on page 242 in your Student Edition. Imagine you could interview the artist about his photography. What would you ask him? Write your questions below.

Example: _Who is the man in the photograph?_

1. Who _____
_____

2. Where _____
_____

3. What _____
_____

4. Why _____
_____

5. When _____
_____

6. How _____
_____

Name _____ Date _____

UNIT 5: Why do we explore new frontiers?

Reading 1: "Early Explorers"

Vocabulary   **Key Words** *Use with Student Edition page 247.*

Write each word in the word box next to its definition.

| civilizations | expeditions | exploration | markets | navigator | trade |

Example: __markets__: areas where people buy and sell goods

1. _____: the officer on a ship or aircraft who plans the route
2. _____: long and carefully organized trips, often to dangerous places
3. _____: a trip to a new place to learn about it
4. _____: buy and sell goods and services
5. _____: societies that are well-organized and developed

Use the words in the word box to complete the sentences.

6. A _____ planned the route the ship would take across the ocean.
7. Many people have studied the ancient _____ of Rome and Greece.
8. The space rovers' _____ of Mars led to exciting discoveries.
9. Early explorers made carefully planned _____ to North and South America.
10. They discovered new _____ in China and South America to exchange goods.

Unit 5 • Reading 1   129

Vocabulary — **Academic Words** *Use with Student Edition page 248.*

Read the paragraph below. Pay attention to the underlined Academic Words.

> My grandparents decided to move to a warmer place. A real estate agent conducted a search for the perfect home. They looked at houses that varied greatly in price and size. They fell in love with a house in Pleasantville, a town that was established in 1695. My grandparents made a down payment on the house and the bank financed the rest. They moved in last month.

Write the Academic Words from the paragraph above next to their correct definitions.

Example: __conducted__ : led or guided

1. _____ : gave money for something

2. _____ : consisting of many different kinds of things

3. _____ : started something new

Use the Academic Words from the paragraph to complete the sentences.

4. The early civilization's diet consisted of _____ fruits, nuts, and fish.

5. A wealthy woman generously _____ my summer at camp so my parents did not have to pay for it.

6. Sarah and I _____ a great friendship during the summer.

7. The explorers _____ a year-long search for the lost gold.

Complete the sentences with your own ideas.

Example: My uncle financed __our trip to New York__.

8. I have a varied collection of _____.

9. A guide conducted me through _____.

10. The rules my teachers established in kindergarten were _____.

130   Unit 5 • Reading 1

Name _____ Date _____

Word Study — Synonyms Use with Student Edition page 249.

> **REMEMBER** A **synonym** is a word with the same meaning or almost the same meaning as another word. For example, *labor* is a synonym for *work*.

Read the words in the chart below. Complete the chart by writing a synonym for each word. Use a thesaurus if needed.

Word	Synonym
cold	freezing
brave	
fast	
orders	
smart	
conversation	

Look at the chart. Write a synonym for each word. Then write a sentence using the synonym. Use a thesaurus if helpful.

Word	Synonym	Sentence
expensive	costly	The sneakers are costly.
sad		
escape		
village		
sleep		
voyage		

Unit 5 • Reading 1

Reading Strategy: Make Generalizations

Use with Student Edition page 249.

> **REMEMBER** When you **make a generalization**, you make a broad statement that encompasses all of the details in a passage. First, ask yourself general questions about the passage.

Read each paragraph and make a generalization about the information.

1. Vasco da Gama was born in Portugal. His father had been a knight and an explorer. When the king of Portugal wanted to find a trade route to India by ocean instead of over land, he gave da Gama a fleet of four ships. While da Gama spent more than two years on the journey, had trouble trading with the goods he had brought, and lost many of his crew, his first mission was considered a success because he found the route the king had wanted around Africa.

   What generalization can you make about Vasco da Gama?

   _____

2. When he was a young man, Samuel de Champlain was a geographer who had a great ability to make predictions about the appearance of unexplored land. His maps, drawings, and descriptions impressed King Henry IV, and he was chosen to be a geographer on a journey to the eastern coast of what is now part of Canada and the United States. One of his settlements became Quebec City, in Canada.

   What generalization can you make about Samuel de Champlain?

   _____

3. Native Americans greatly respected the Earth and believed its land was sacred. They believed the land was created for animals and people to share. They did not believe that it could be owned, bought, or sold. Native Americans were thankful for the land and all that it provided to them. To show their respect, they only used what they needed; they didn't believe in wasting the Earth's resources.

   What generalization can you make about how Native American tribes viewed Earth?

   _____

Name _____ Date _____

Comprehension *Use with Student Edition page 254.*

Choose the best answer for each item. Circle the letter of the correct answer.

1. The Phoenicians explored other lands to find _____.

   a. shipbuilders   b. new markets   c. Lebanon

2. The Vikings were from _____.

   a. Scandinavia   b. Venice, Italy   c. Britain

3. The Silk Road connected Europe with _____.

   a. Sierra Leone   b. the Spice Islands   c. China

4. Henry the Navigator was _____.

   a. an Italian explorer   b. a prince of Portugal   c. a storyteller from Italy

5. Sacagawea was valuable to Lewis and Clark because she could _____.

   a. trap animals   b. translate Shoshone and Hidatsa   c. row a boat

Extension *Use with Student Edition page 255.*

Write the names of five explorers that interest you. Then research their voyages. In the chart, list the places they explored.

Explorer	The Place the Explorer Traveled to
Marco Polo	the Silk Road

Unit 5 • Reading 1

Grammar Past Perfect: *had* + Past Participle

Use with Student Edition page 256.

> **REMEMBER** You can use the **past perfect** and the simple past to tell about past events. The past perfect tells about an event that happened earlier and is formed with ***had* + the past participle**. Form regular past participles by adding *-d* or *-ed* to the base form of the verb. Many past participles are irregular, such as *give / given*, *have / had*, and *be / been* and must be memorized. The simple past tells about the event that came later.

Underline the first event and circle the second event in each sentence.

Example: Paul had called me three times. (I finally called him back.)

1. I got to the party. It had already ended.
2. I had waited for hours. Josie finally showed up.
3. She hadn't finished her test. The teacher took it anyway.
4. She had worked for hours. Then she realized it was morning.

Complete each sentence with the past perfect or the simple past form of the verb in parentheses.

Example: I (see) __had seen__ that movie already. I didn't want to watch it again.

5. Linda had dropped off her jacket. Then she (go) _____ to school.

6. By 5:30, I had done five loads of laundry. Then I (watch) _____ some TV.

7. I rode my bike to the library. It (close) _____ already.

8. (receive) _____ you _____ the package yet? I mailed it on Thursday.

134 Unit 5 • Reading 1

Name _____ Date _____

Compound and Complex Sentences with Past Perfect

Use with Student Edition page 257.

> **REMEMBER** **Compound sentences** are made up of two independent clauses connected with a coordinating conjunction such as *and* or *but*. **Complex sentences** are made up of one independent clause and at least one dependent clause, which begins with a subordinating conjunction such as *after*, *before*, or *when*. In both compound and complex sentences, you can use the **past perfect** to tell about an earlier event and the simple past to tell about an event that happened after that.

Underline the past perfect verb in each sentence. Circle the simple past verb. Then decide if the sentence is compound or complex.

Example: Before Lewis and Clark (made) their journey, no white or black Americans had traveled through the Northwest. _____*complex*_____

1. Some Native Americans had never seen a white man before the explorers visited. _____

2. When they ended their expedition, Lewis and Clark had still not found a water route to the Pacific. _____

3. Sacagawea hadn't wanted to go with them, but in the end she went. _____

4. After the explorers had arrived, they realized how difficult it would be. _____

5. Many months had passed, and the explorers were tired. _____

6. Lewis and Clark reached the camp after they had endured many hardships. _____

7. Sacagawea had been a member of the Shoshone tribe, but she was kidnapped by the Hidatsa. _____

8. It was spring, and Sacagawea and her baby had joined the expedition. _____

Unit 5 • Reading 1

Writing: Write a Cause-and-Effect Paragraph

Use with Student Edition pages 258–259.

Complete your own cause and effect chart about how an event, situation, or problem leads to certain results or effects.

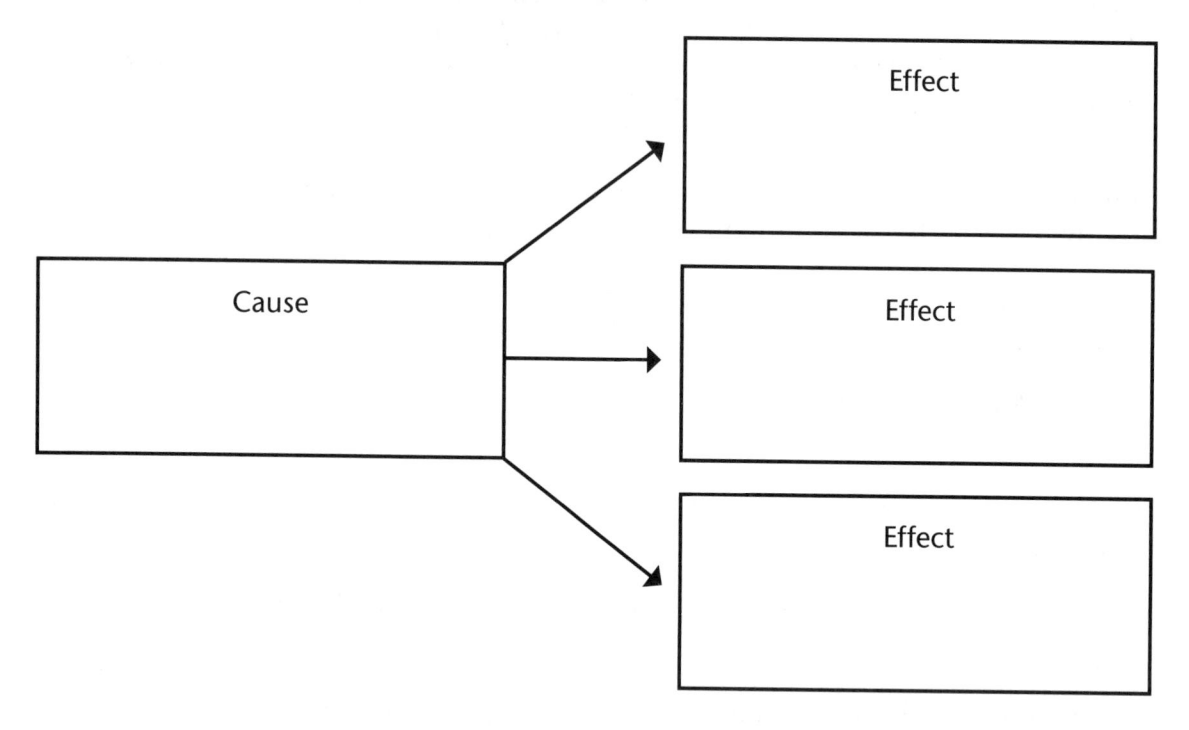

```
                    ┌─────────────┐
                   →│   Effect    │
                    └─────────────┘
┌─────────┐         ┌─────────────┐
│  Cause  │────────→│   Effect    │
└─────────┘         └─────────────┘
                    ┌─────────────┐
                   →│   Effect    │
                    └─────────────┘
```

Have your partner complete (✓) the Peer Review Checklist. Use this feedback to help you edit your final draft.

Peer Review Checklist

- ☐ Does the paragraph explain a cause-and-effect relationship?
- ☐ Does it present information in an order that makes sense?
- ☐ Does it include signal words such as *because* and *therefore*?
- ☐ Do sentences vary in length and pattern?
- ☐ Is the past perfect used correctly?
- ☐ Could changes be made to improve the paragraph?

Name _____ Date _____

UNIT 5: Why do we explore new frontiers?

Reading 2: "Navigation Then and Now: Using GPS"

Vocabulary — **Key Words** *Use with Student Edition page 261.*

Write each word in the box next to its definition.

| calculate | depicted | expeditions | magnetic | mariners | navigation |

Example: __navigation__ : the act of finding which way to go

1. _____ : long journeys to unfamiliar places
2. _____ : able to attract something
3. _____ : to use numbers to find a total for something
4. _____ : to show in a picture or describe in words
5. _____ : people who sail the sea

Use the words in the word box to complete the sentences.

6. The _____ force between the two objects caused them to stick together.
7. Did you _____ my portion of the dinner cost?
8. My Uncle Esteban used to take us on long _____ through the woods near his house.
9. Do you use your phone or a paper map for _____ ?
10. The _____ were at sea for three months.
11. Some politicians are _____ by cartoonists in an unflattering way.

Unit 5 • Reading 2

Vocabulary
Academic Words *Use with Student Edition page 262.*

Read the paragraph below. Pay attention to the underlined Academic Words.

> Last summer, I went to a camp that teaches you how to survive in the woods. Even though it was a little scary, I trusted the camp director because the program was <u>founded</u> more than 20 years ago. First, we had to put away all the <u>equipment</u> we use every day, such as our smartphones, our watches, and even our plastic water bottles! Then he challenged us to make a <u>chart</u> showing what we knew about survival and what we wanted to learn. By the end of the week, I could easily go into the woods without getting lost and find food to eat. The campers received a small pocket knife as a <u>symbol</u> of our achievement.

Match each word with its definition.

Example: __a__ chart   a. a diagram to convey information

_____ 1. equipment   b. started or organized

_____ 2. founded   c. things you carry with you to do a job

_____ 3. symbol   d. something that stands for something else

Use the Academic Words from the exercise above to complete the sentences.

4. I couldn't read the language, but I could understand the _____ on the sign.

5. This _____ will show us which trails to follow when we go hiking.

6. The nature organization was _____ in 1905.

7. Putting satellites in space requires a lot of special _____.

Complete the sentences with your own ideas.

8. A chart can be helpful to use when _____.

9. My favorite camping equipment includes _____.

10. A symbol that can be easily recognized is _____.

Name _____ Date _____

Word Study Spelling *ie / ei* Use with Student Edition page 263.

REMEMBER Words spelled with the vowels *ie* have the long *e* sound, as in *chief*. Words spelled with the vowels *ei* have the long *a* sound as in *neighbor*.

Read the words in the box. Then write the words in the correct column in the chart.

| field eighteen freighter yield thief rein grief piece neighbor sleigh |

Words with the long *e* sound spelled *ie*	Words with the long *a* sound spelled *ei*
field	

Write the letter-sound pattern in the words.

Example: pr<u>ie</u>st ___long e sound spelled ie___

1. brief _____
2. berries _____
3. fierce _____
4. cities _____
5. weighty _____

Unit 5 • Reading 2

Reading Strategy | Take Notes about Main Ideas and Key Details

Use with Student Edition page 263.

> **REMEMBER** Taking notes, or writing down important information, helps you understand and remember what you are reading.

Read the following paragraph. Underline important information, such as facts. Then write notes about these facts on the lines below.

> Long before there were computers and satellites, people used compasses to help them find their way from place to place. A compass is a small instrument that contains a magnet. When you hold the compass in your hand, it always points toward the North Pole. Many centuries ago, some of the world's greatest explorers traveled long distances using only a compass as a guide. Even today, sailors and hikers use a compass to help them find their way.

_____
_____
_____
_____
_____
_____
_____
_____

Name _____ Date _____

Comprehension *Use with Student Edition page 268.*

Choose the best answer for each item. Circle the letter of the correct answer.

1. In order to function, GPS needs _____.

   a. magnets **b.** satellites **c.** compasses

2. Ancient mariners used _____ for navigation.

   a. space **b.** expeditions **c.** the sun

3. John Harrison invented a sea clock that led to the invention of the _____.

   a. chronometer **b.** compass **c.** sextant

4. A lodestone has the properties of a _____.

   a. magnet **b.** scale **c.** needle

5. You can hold a compass anywhere on Earth and it will point _____.

   a. upward **b.** south **c.** north

Extension *Use with Student Edition page 269.*

Find two different maps in a classroom reference book. Copy the maps here, using different colors to show different features. Be sure to add symbols and a compass showing north, south, east, and west.

Unit 5 • Reading 2

Grammar — Imperatives and *will* for Instructions

Use with Student Edition page 270.

> **REMEMBER** Use an **imperative** to give instructions. The simple present is used and the subject is *you*, but it is not stated. To form the negative, add *do not* or *don't* before the verb. You can also use the future with *will* to give instructions, especially to list the items needed in projects and recipes or to explain what is going to happen next.

Underline the imperative sentence in each group of sentences.

Example: What will you wear? <u>Wear the blue shirt.</u> You wear the blue shirt often.

1. Will you say your name? Say your name. Everyone said his or her name.
2. Don't lose the key. Did you lose the key? The key is lost.
3. Do you sit in that chair? Does she sit next to you? Please sit with me.
4. I didn't understand you. You speak so fast. Speak slowly, please.
5. Can you think of an answer? Think of an answer. No one can think of an answer.

Write sentences using *will* and the verb in parentheses to give instructions.

Example: (see) <u>You will see a stoplight on the corner.</u>

6. (tell) _____

7. (take) _____

8. (teach) _____

9. (write) _____

10. (call) _____

Name _____ Date _____

Grammar — Sequence Words, Phrases, and Clauses

Use with Student Edition page 271.

> **REMEMBER** **Sequence words and phrases** such as *first, then, next, after that,* and *finally* describe the order in which events take place. *First* and *finally* introduce the first and last things that happened. *Then, next,* and *after that* introduce anything that happened in between. Most of these sequence words and phrases take a comma after them, but *then* does not.
>
> Subordinate adverbial time conjunctions such as *after, before,* and *when* can also be used to give instructions. Use them in subordinate **clauses** before or after a main clause. A comma follows the clause when it begins the sentence.

The sentences below present a series of events in the wrong order. Write *First, Second, Then, Next,* or *Finally* to show the correct order.

1. _____ we found seats in the movie theater.

2. _____ we stood in line to buy tickets.

3. _____ we watched the movie.

4. _____ we went to the movie theater.

5. _____ we bought our tickets.

Circle the correct word to complete the following sentences.

6. (Second, / When) you get to the stoplight, turn right.

7. Make a hole. (Then / Finally,) put in the plant. Next, water it.

8. (After / After that,) you have finished that, close the door.

9. (Now / Third,) you will see a bright light.

10. (Before / Last,) you plant the seed, water the ground.

Unit 5 • Reading 2

Writing **Write an Instructional Paragraph**

Use with Student Edition pages 272–273.

Complete your own sequence chart about how to do something.

First

↓

Then

↓

Next

↓

Finally

Have your partner complete (✓) the Peer Review Checklist. Use this feedback to help you edit your final draft.

Peer Review Checklist

☐ Does the paragraph give instructions for doing an activity?
☐ Are steps presented in a logical order?
☐ Do sequence words and phrases help clarify the steps?
☐ Are imperatives used correctly?
☐ Are words spelled correctly?
☐ Could changes be made to improve the paragraph?

Name _____ Date _____

UNIT 5: Why do we explore new frontiers?

Reading 3: "A World within the Hollow"

Vocabulary — Literary Words
Use with Student Edition page 275.

REMEMBER Onomatopoeia is the use of words that imitate the sounds they represent. **Hyperbole** is a way of describing something by exaggerating on purpose.

Label each sentence to tell if it uses onomatopoeia or hyperbole.

Onomatopoeia or hyperbole?	Sentence
onomatopoeia	Her high heels click-clacked down the hallway.
1.	That basketball player can sink a basket from a mile away.
2.	The thunder boomed in the dark, angry sky.
3.	He's so smart that he can read a book with his eyes closed.
4.	The boy slurped up the melting ice cream.
5.	The gong of the bells was so loud, I couldn't hear anything else.

Read the passage about Wyatt Earp. Label the examples of onomatopoeia and hyperbole.

Wyatt Earp was born in 1848 in Illinois. It was said that he could fire a gun when he was only one year old. I don't know about that. I do know that as a boy he practiced shooting at targets every day. (6.)

All afternoon you could hear the pop, pop, pop and crack of his gun shots. Most were right on target. (7.)

As a young man, he left home for Kansas. His skill with a gun got him the job of sheriff in Dodge City.

He was a good lawman because bad guys feared him. All they had to do was hear the jingle of his spurs and they ran. (8.)

Earp was an ordinary fellow, but when he faced an outlaw it was as if he were a ten-foot-tall, mean-looking giant. His hard stare was so scary, he rarely had to use his gun. (9.) (10.)

Vocabulary — **Academic Words** Use with Student Edition page 276.

Read the paragraph below. Pay attention to the underlined Academic Words.

> When you move to a new school, you will go through a period of adjustment. At first, you may feel <u>unique</u> because everyone is talking about "the new kid." After a few days, the other students carry on with their regular friendships and pay less attention to you, making you feel almost <u>invisible</u>. This might seem bad, but it actually gives you some time to think. Before you join a sports team or club, consider the <u>fundamental</u> interests you want to share with your friends. Come up with some <u>alternative</u> ways to meet new friends that will challenge others to talk to people they wouldn't normally hang out with. You could form a study group, a bike-to-school group, or a Friday night movie club. Don't be shy about asking. Remember, some people in your new school have been waiting for a friend like you!

Match each word with its definition.

Example: __d__ invisible   a. basic, important

_____ 1. fundamental   b. one-of-a-kind

_____ 2. unique   c. other, different

_____ 3. alternative   d. not able to be seen

Use the Academic Words from the exercise above to complete the sentences.

4. Their love of science fiction books was _____ to their friendship.

5. Most contact lenses are so thin, they're nearly _____.

6. Nell's skateboard stands out because she has so many _____ stickers on it.

7. One _____ to meat is tofu.

Complete the sentences with your own ideas.

8. The most unique person in my family is _____.

9. Some fundamental things students need to learn are _____.

10. If I can't have my favorite meal, the next best alternative is _____.

Name _____ Date _____

Word Study — Frequently Misspelled Words

Use with Student Edition page 277.

> **REMEMBER** Some words in English are often spelled incorrectly because they are pronounced the same as other words. For example, *air* means "atmosphere" and *err* is "to make a mistake." The words sound the same, but they have different meanings.

Write the definition for each pair of frequently misspelled words.

Words	Definitions
a lot, allot	many, divide
1. alter, altar	
2. allowed, aloud	
3. break, brake	
4. breadth, breath	
5. all together, altogether	

Underline the word that correctly completes each sentence. Then define both words in parenthesis.

Example: (<u>Do</u>, Due) be careful when you cross the street.
  Do means to perform an action. Due means caused by.

6. We measure the (ark, arc) of the circle.
   _____

7. My father bought the (board, bored) from the lumber yard.
   _____

8. The trainer puts the (bridal, bridle) on the horse.
   _____

9. The (capital, capitol) of New York State is Albany.
   _____

10. The soldiers fought a (dual, duel) with swords.
    _____

Unit 5 • Reading 3   147

Reading Strategy | **Skim**

Use with Student Edition page 277.

> **REMEMBER** When you **skim** a text, you read it very quickly to get a general understanding of what it's about.

Skim the passage. Then answer the questions.

> In the late 1800s, many Americans traveled west looking for a better life. They left poverty behind in the hopes of making money as farmers. Often, an entire family packed its belongings into a wagon, which traveled across the open plains. The rough journey took many months as the wagons jolted and bumped over the wild land.
>
> In the 1890s, the U.S. government gave away unclaimed prairie land for free. However, for people to own this land, they had to agree to build a house on the land and to farm it for five years. This practice was known as a "land rush."
>
> On the day of a land rush, thousands of people sat on their horses and waited for a cannon to fire. When they heard the shot, people raced to claim a piece of land. The first person to claim the land owned it. Some people got good land, while others did not. Some got there too late and got no land at all.

1. Circle the topic sentence in each paragraph.

   _____

2. In your own words, explain the main idea of each paragraph.

   _____

   _____

   _____

3. Summarize the entire passage in one sentence.

   _____

4. How might skimming a passage before reading it help you to understand the text better?

   _____

Name _____ Date _____

Comprehension   *Use with Student Edition page 284.*

Choose the best answer for each item. Circle the letter of the correct answer.

1. Violet feels _____ because Yates moved away.

    a. relieved   **b.** invisible   **c.** lonely

2. The last time Violet went to Roni's house, Roni only wanted to _____.

    a. watch birds   **b.** play video games   **c.** take pictures

3. Violet finds the path to an alternate reality in a _____.

    a. tree trunk   **b.** waterfall   **c.** photo studio

4. In the regular world, Roni is upset with Violet because Violet _____ her.

    a. made fun of   **b.** told lies about   **c.** rejected

5. The old tree was cut down by _____.

    a. Roni   **b.** forest workers   **c.** hikers

Response to Literature   *Use with Student Edition page 285.*

Think of a scene in your alternate reality story. Illustrate it. Then include dialogue for the people or animals in the scene. Write the dialogue on a separate piece of paper.

Unit 5 • Reading 3   149

Grammar Adjectival Phrases: Comparatives

Use with Student Edition page 286.

REMEMBER You can compare one person, place, or thing to another with a **comparative adjective**. Form a comparative adjective by adding *-er* or using *more* before the adjective. Irregular comparatives include *good / better* and *bad / worse*. *Than* precedes the second part of the comparison. When the second comparison is obvious, you can omit it. In addition to comparatives, you can also use *as . . . as* to say that two things are equal; you can use *not as . . . as* to show that two things are not equal. You can use *less* to mean the opposite of *-er* or *more*.

Complete the sentences with the comparative form of the adjective in parentheses, using *-er* or *more*. Then rewrite the sentences giving them the opposite meaning. (Remember the opposite of *good* is *bad*.)

Example: (helpful) Your brother is __more helpful__ than you are.
   Your brother is less helpful than you are.

1. (hot) This summer is much _____ than last summer.

   _____

2. (difficult) Mr. Bronson's class is _____ than Ms. Sheild's.

   _____

3. (good) My new coffee maker is so much _____ than my old one.

   _____

Complete the sentences with *as . . . as* or *not as . . . as*. Use contractions when possible.

Example: Dogs are __not as__ intelligent __as__ cats. Cats are much smarter.

4. No other U.S. president is _____ famous _____ George Washington. He is known all around the world.

5. My sister is _____ tall _____ I am. I am much taller.

6. Mark is _____ good at math _____ Brett is, but Mark is better at languages.

Name _____ Date _____

Grammar — Adjectival Phrases: Superlatives

Use with Student Edition page 287.

> **REMEMBER** Use a **superlative adjective** to compare one person, place, or thing to others in a group. Form a superlative adjective by adding *-est* or using the word *most* before the adjective. Irregular superlatives include *good / the best* and *bad / the worst*. The phrase *one of the* is often used with a plural noun and a superlative adjective to talk about one out of a group. You can use *least* to mean the opposite of *-est* or *most*.

Complete the following sentences with the superlative form of the adjective in parentheses, using *-est* or *most*. Then rewrite the sentences giving them the opposite meaning.

Example: (fast) My bike is the _____fastest_____ bike on the block.
My bike is the least fast bike on the block.

1. (sleepy) This is the _____ I have ever felt in my life.
   _____

2. (expensive) His car is the _____ car in the parking lot.
   _____

3. (interesting) That was one of the _____ movies I've ever seen.
   _____

4. (good) The new restaurant in town is the _____ one in town.
   _____

5. (happy) Sandra has lived in many cities, but she's _____ living in Boston.
   _____

6. (good) Our team is the _____ among all the soccer teams in our division.
   _____

Unit 5 • Reading 3

Writing Write a Classifying Paragraph

Use with Student Edition pages 288–289.

Complete your own two- or three-column chart showing how something can be classified.

Characteristics		

Have your partner complete (✓) the Peer Review Checklist. Use this feedback to help you edit your final draft.

Peer Review Checklist
- ☐ Does the paragraph classify information?
- ☐ Are similar items grouped together by category?
- ☐ Are the features of each category clearly described and explained?
- ☐ Do sentences vary in length and pattern?
- ☐ Are comparatives and superlatives used correctly?
- ☐ Could changes be made to improve the paragraph?

Name _____ Date _____

Writing Workshop *Use with Student Edition pages 294–297.*

Organize your ideas in the graphic organizer below.

1.

2.

3.

4.

5.

6.

7.

8.

9.

10.

Have your partner complete (✓) the Peer Review Checklist. Use this feedback to help you edit your final draft.

Peer Review Checklist
- ☐ Did the essay teach me how to do something?
- ☐ Were the steps easy to follow?
- ☐ Was the writing lively and engaging?
- ☐ Did sequence words help me better understand the process?
- ☐ Were familiar words spelled correctly?
- ☐ Could changes be made to improve the essay?

Unit 5 • Writing Workshop

Learning Log — Use after completing Student Edition page 298.

Underline the vocabulary items you know and can use well. Review and practice any you haven't underlined. Underline them when you know them well.

Literary Words	Key Words	Academic Words
hyperbole	civilizations	conducted
onomatopoeia	expeditions	established
	exploration	financed
	markets	varied
	navigator	chart
	trade	equipment
	calculate	founded
	depicted	symbol
	expeditions	alternative
	magnetic	fundamental
	mariners	invisible
	navigation	unique

Put a check by the skills you can perform well. Review and practice any you haven't checked off. Check them off when you can perform them well.

Skills	I can . . .
Word Study	☐ use synonyms. ☐ spell words with *-ie* and *-ei* as in *brief* and *height*. ☐ identify frequently misspelled words and use them correctly.
Reading Strategies	☐ make generalizations. ☐ take notes about main ideas and key details. ☐ skim.
Grammar	☐ use the past perfect; use compound/complex sentences with past perfect correctly. ☐ use imperatives correctly; use sequence words, phrases, and clauses. ☐ use adjectival phrases; use comparatives and superlatives.
Writing	☐ write a cause-and-effect paragraph. ☐ write an instructional paragraph. ☐ write a classifying paragraph. ☐ write an instructional essay.

Name _____ Date _____

Test Preparation

Test 1

DIRECTIONS
Read this selection. Then answer the questions that follow it.

Make a Poster

Today students are reading about what they will need to do to prepare a poster as a project. The selection below is about researching information to include on the poster.

1   You will need to research information for your poster. You can use encyclopedias, newspaper or __1__ articles, nonfiction books, and the internet. Use only internet sites that have been approved by your teacher.

2   You cannot use someone else's words as your own. If you find a(n) __2__ you want to use on your poster, you have two choices. You can write the information in your own words, or you can quote the original author. In both cases, you must cite the source. If you do use someone else's words as your own, or if you fail to cite the source of an idea, you will automatically __3__ an F on the project.

3   For each encyclopedia, newspaper, magazine article, book, or internet site you use, you must make a source card. Use the sample source cards in your poster packet as a __4__.

1 **A** notebook
   B textbook
   C magazine
   D brochure

2 **A** poster
   B idea
   C homework
   D television

3 **A** understand
   B research
   C receive
   D imply

4 **A** task
   B student
   C leader
   D guide

Test Preparation   155

Test 2

DIRECTIONS
Read this selection. Then answer the questions that follow it.

New Frontiers in Science

1   Ivan went to the school library to find facts about a new frontier in science. Mrs. Walton, his science teacher, said a new frontier could be anything new that scientists were studying. He remembered seeing an interesting news story about something called the Urban Heat Effect. Ivan decided to write his report about that topic. He read many articles and websites to find enough facts. Then he wrote a paper and included a picture. Below is what Ivan wrote.

Urban Heat

2   Cities, or urban areas, today are usually hotter than the countryside. In summer, cities have temperatures that average 6 to 8 degrees Fahrenheit higher than temperatures outside cities. This is called the Urban Heat Effect.

3   Cities have more concrete, buildings, and dark-colored roofs. These objects and others like sidewalks and roads soak up the day's heat. Then they release, or let go of, the heat at the end of the day. This means that the greatest differences in temperature between cities and the country usually happen at night.

1 Paragraph 3 is mainly about —
   A the causes of the Urban Heat Effect
   B Ivan's project
   C the articles Ivan read to find facts
   D the difference in temperature in the summer

2 In paragraph 2, what word or words help the reader know what <u>urban areas</u> means?
   A usually hotter
   B cities
   C today
   D countryside

3 According to Ivan's report, which object soaks up heat in cities?
   A cars
   B trees
   C stores
   D sidewalks

4 The reader can conclude that Ivan chose to write about the Urban Heat Effect because —
   A his teacher assigned the topic
   B he asked the librarian for topic ideas
   C he read about the topic in class
   D he was interested in the topic

Name _____ Date _____

Test 3

DIRECTIONS
Read this selection. Then answer the questions that follow it.

Choosing Cell Phones

1   Buying a cell phone might feel like exploring a new frontier. However, if you study the information about cell phones before you start shopping for one, finding a phone is really not difficult.

Phones

2   Cell phones have the same features as home phones. For example, they have voice mail and caller ID. But cell phones also have features that home phones do not have. Since they are little computers, they can store a large amount of information. Some are so powerful that they can run an office. However, the cell phone network is limited: while cell phones usually work well in cities, they may not work at all in the country.

Accessories

3   The price of a phone increases as you add <u>accessories</u>. Basic phones with few extra features cost around $100. They usually have features such as contact lists, caller ID, and games. Phones with accessories like longer-lasting batteries, cameras, and MP3 players can cost as much as $500. Before you buy, think carefully about which accessories you really need on your phone. Then decide how much money you are willing to pay for those accessories.

Plans

4   Most companies offer a variety of cell phone plans. Plans give you a certain number of minutes to talk at certain times of day for one monthly fee. A fee is money you pay for something. For example, a plan might include 100 minutes to be used between 8:00 a.m. and 8:00 p.m. for $50.00 a month. Companies also give you a calling area. This is usually the city and surrounding cities where you live. Companies may charge you more money if you make a call when you are not in your calling area. Some companies have plans that do not have a monthly fee. Instead, you pay a certain amount for each call you make, depending on how many minutes you use for the call. Sometimes these calls are more expensive.

1 Look at this chart.

Accessories	Cell Phones	Home Phones
Voice mail	X	X
Caller ID	X	X
Network in Cities	X	X
Network in the Country		X
Longer-lasting Batteries	X	

Which of these also belongs in the chart?

A more expensive
B difficult to use
C powerful enough to run an office
D cameras

2 Paragraph 3 is mainly about —

A the extra features of cell phones
B the cost of cell phone plans
C the features of home phones
D competition among companies

3 In paragraph 3, what words help the reader know what <u>accessories</u> means?

A extra features
B price of a phone
C goes up
D basic phones

4 According to the article, what should you think about before you decide how much you will pay for a cell phone?

A competition of companies
B the accessories you need
C longer lasting batteries
D MP3 players

5 In paragraph 4, the example helps the reader understand —

A calling areas
B a cell phone plan
C fees
D amount of minutes

Name _____ Date _____

Visual Literacy: Smithsonian American Art Museum *Use with Student Edition pages 300–301.*

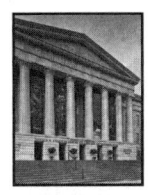

Learning to Look

Look at *Vaquero* by Luis Jiménez on page 301 in your Student Edition. How many objects can you spot in this sculpture? List your answers below. State facts, not opinions.

Example: a cowboy

1. _____

2. _____

3. _____

Interpretation

Look at *Vaquero* again. Imagine that the cowboy is real. What would he tell you about the sculpture? Write your answers below.

_____

_____

_____

_____

_____

_____

Unit 5 • Visual Literacy: Smithsonian American Art Museum

COMPARE & CONTRAST

Look at *Corn Dance, Taos Pueblo* by Norman S. Chamberlain on page 300 in your Student Edition. Write three details about the hooded figures in the painting.

Example: Some of the hooded figures are facing away from others.

1. _____
2. _____
3. _____

Write three details about the people who are not wearing hoods.

4. _____
5. _____
6. _____

7. How are the two groups similar?

   _____
   _____
   _____

8. How are the two groups different?

   _____
   _____
   _____

Name _____ Date _____

UNIT 6: How do we know what is true?

Reading 1: "How Glooskap Found the Summer" / "Persephone and the Pomegranate Seeds"

Vocabulary — **Literary Words** *Use with Student Edition page 305.*

> **REMEMBER** A **myth** is a fictional story that is told to explain a natural event, like wind or rain.
> **Example:** Ancient Greeks believed that the god Zeus controlled thunder.
> A male **hero** or female **heroine** is a character in a story whose actions are inspiring or noble.
> **Example:** Superwoman stopped the fire and saved the day.

Label the following people as heroes, heroines, or both.

Situation	Label
Example: police officers	heroes and heroines
1. male firefighters	
2. teenage boy who rescued kids after bridge collapse	
3. women who work for rescue services	
4. mother who led family out of burning house	
5. male rescuers of trapped miner	
6. female and male main characters in books	

Read the newspaper story. Label details in it as myth, heroine, or hero.

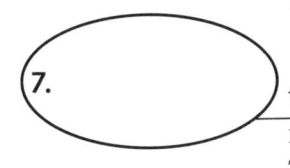

Twins Help Neighbors Reach Safety

ANYWHERE, USA, Aug. 2—When the river running through this small town overran its shores due to a rainstorm, Claire and Ben Sherman went to work. The 13-year-old twins took a small rowboat from their waterlogged garage. Then, for hours, they went from house to house lifting stranded people into the little vessel to be rowed to safety. A scared woman they rescued said that Poseidon himself must have been angry and caused the rainstorm.

By the end of the day, everyone was safe. "Those kids were brave," said an admiring neighbor. "Yes," added another, "they are our very own Hercules."

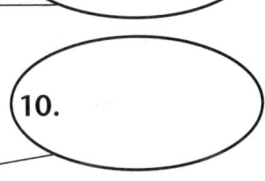

Unit 6 • Reading 1 161

Vocabulary   **Academic Words** Use with Student Edition page 306.

Read the paragraph below. Pay attention to the underlined Academic Words.

> Despite their role as rulers, the ancient Greek gods often behaved like regular people. The gods lived on Mount Olympus, but they often visited the human world. Some gods used their powers to manipulate the actions of people. They did foolish things and punished those who made them angry. Other Greek gods were good and worked to restore peace and happiness to the human world. When we evaluate these myths today, we can infer that sometimes the storytellers wanted us to see how imperfect gods and humans were.

Write the Academic Words from the paragraph above next to their correct definitions.

Example: _manipulate_: make someone do exactly what you want by deceiving or influencing him or her

1. _____: judge something's worth

2. _____: draw a conclusion based on facts

3. _____: function or part

Use Academic Words from the paragraph to complete the sentences.

4. I will play the _____ of Zeus in the school play.

5. My older sister can _____ me by talking me into doing something I don't want to do.

6. We could _____ that she used to live in that neighborhood from some things she said about the shops and restaurants.

Complete the sentences with your own ideas.

Example: I can infer from looking at my friend's photos that he/she likes _reading, playing football, and hanging out with friends_.

7. I don't like being manipulated by _____.

8. At home, my main role is _____.

9. To evaluate how good or trustworthy a website is, I _____.

Name _____ Date _____

Word Study — Antonyms *Use with Student Edition page 307.*

> **REMEMBER** An **antonym** is a word that means the opposite of another word. For example, the antonym for the word *day* is *night*.

Look at the chart. Write antonyms for the words.

Word	Antonym
Example: big	small
1. new	
2. happy	
3. quietly	
4. beautiful	
5. after	

Look at the chart. Write the antonyms for the words. Then write sentences using the antonyms.

Word	Antonym	Sentence
Example: never	always	I always play with my puppy after school.
6. sick		
7. under		
8. empty		
9. last		
10. easy		

Unit 6 • Reading 1

Reading Strategy | Compare and Contrast

Use with Student Edition page 307.

> **REMEMBER** When you compare and contrast, you tell what is similar and different about two things, people, or situations.

Read the paragraphs. Then answer the questions.

> The United States and China are nearly equal in the size of their territory. However, China has a much larger population than the United States does. China's population is over one billion people. The United States has more than 300 million people.

1. Based on the passage, in what way are China and the United States alike?

   _____

2. Based on the passage, in what way are China and the United States different?

   _____

> Julio and his friend Alex are great at basketball. They sometimes play after school when they are bored, and the basketball coach is always trying to get them to join the team. However, Julio's favorite sport is football, and Alex's favorite sport is tennis. They enjoy themselves most when they are playing the games they love.

3. Based on the passage, in what way are Alex and Julio alike?

   _____

   _____

4. Based on the passage, in what way are Alex and Julio different?

   _____

   _____

5. How can the skill of comparing and contrasting help you to understand a text?

   _____

   _____

Name _____ Date _____

Comprehension Use with Student Edition page 312.

Choose the best answer for each item. Circle the letter of the correct answer.

1. The leader of the Wawaniki people was named _____.

   a. Glooskap   b. Summer   c. Persephone

2. Winter tried to trick Glooskap by making him _____.

   a. feel cold   b. fall asleep   c. swim in the river

3. Demeter is the goddess of _____.

   a. hunting   b. love   c. agriculture

4. Pluto gave Persephone _____.

   a. pomegranate seeds   b. red flowers   c. a horse

5. After Persephone ate the seeds, she had to stay in the Underworld for _____.

   a. one hundred years   b. the rest of her life   c. six months out of the year

Response to Literature Use with Student Edition page 313.

Pick a character from one of the myths that you find especially interesting. Draw a picture of the character.

Unit 6 • Reading 1

Grammar: Reported Speech: Statements and Questions

Use with Student Edition page 314.

REMEMBER You can use a **direct quotation** or **reported speech** to explain what someone has said. A direct quotation expresses the person's exact words and is enclosed in quotation marks. There are no quotation marks in reported speech, and the person's words may be paraphrased.
In reported speech, *that* often comes after a reporting verb such as *said*, and the verb tense and pronouns usually change. When you want to mention the listener, you can use a direct object with the reporting verb *told*. To report questions, use the reporting verb *asked*. Word order for questions in reported speech is the same as in statements; the subject comes before the verb. For *Wh-* questions, word order is *Wh-* question + subject + verb.

Finish the sentences using reported speech. Remember to make any necessary changes to verbs and pronouns.

Example: Peter: "I cleaned the house already."

Peter said _that he had cleaned the house already._

1. John: "Maura is at home."

   John said _____.

2. Max: "Frank is reading the newspaper."

   Max told me _____.

3. Ron: "Where does Maria usually park her car?"

   Ron asked _____.

4. Andy: "Is Olive having lunch with Sissy?"

   Andy asked _____.

5. Justin: "What are you doing?"

   Justin asked _____.

Past Progressive with Adverbial Clauses
Use with Student Edition page 315.

> **REMEMBER** You can use the past progressive with an adverbial *when* clause in the simple past to express an action that was interrupted by another. The clause in the past progressive tells about the first action in progress that was interrupted. The adverbial *when* clause in the simple past tells about the action that interrupted the first. When the adverbial *when* clause begins a sentence, use a comma after the clause.

Underline the past progressive verb and circle the simple past verb in each sentence.

Example: I <u>was reading</u> a book when the phone (rang).

1. When I saw the bird, it was flying south.
2. We were walking in the park when we heard thunder.
3. When Henry's mother walked in, he was cleaning his room.
4. The boys were throwing a ball in the house when they broke a vase.

Complete the sentences with the simple past or the past progressive form of the verb in parentheses.

Example: I (chop) __was chopping__ vegetables when I (cut) __cut__ my thumb.

5. My uncle (drive) _____ on the highway when he (get) _____ into an accident.
6. When Dick (learn) _____ about the flight change, he (drive) _____ to the airport.
7. We (have) _____ lunch when the fire alarm (go) _____ off.
8. Carl (talk) _____ on his cell phone when his battery (die) _____.

Unit 6 • Reading 1

Writing Write an Introductory Paragraph

Use with Student Edition pages 316–317.

Complete your own inverted pyramid to narrow down your topic.

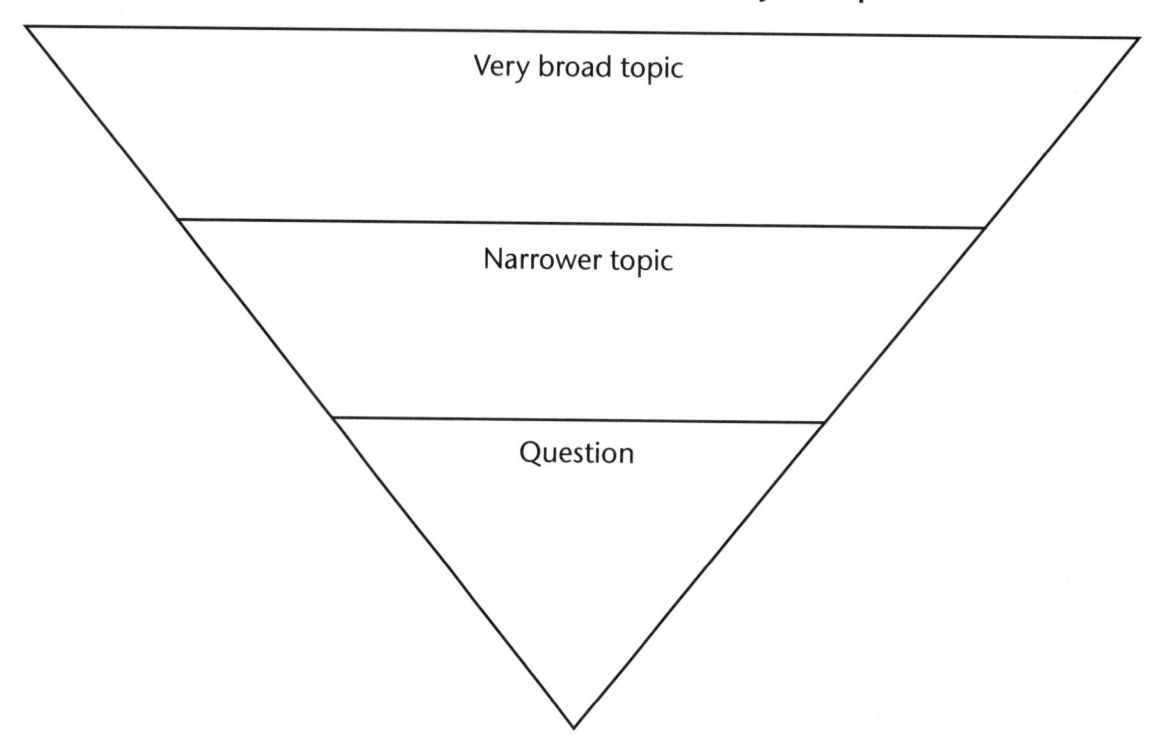

- Very broad topic
- Narrower topic
- Question

Have your partner complete (✓) the Peer Review Checklist. Use this feedback to help you edit your final draft.

Peer Review Checklist
- ☐ Does the paragraph focus on a culture's arts or crafts?
- ☐ Has the writer stated the topic clearly?
- ☐ Does the first sentence capture the reader's attention?
- ☐ Does the writing voice show knowledge of the topic?
- ☐ Are the past progressive and reported speech presented correctly?
- ☐ Could changes be made to improve the paragraph?

Name _____ Date _____

UNIT 6 — How do we know what is true?

Reading 2: "Early Astronomers"

Vocabulary — **Key Words** *Use with Student Edition page 319.*

Write each word in the box next to its definition.

| constellations | discoveries | galaxy | phenomenon | solar system | telescope |

Example: <u>constellations</u>: groups of stars that form patterns and have names

1. _____: something that happens and is unusual and difficult to understand

2. _____: a piece of equipment that is shaped like a tube and is used to make faraway objects look bigger and closer

3. _____: a system of planets, moons, etc., that move around the sun

4. _____: facts or things that someone finds out about that weren't known before

5. _____: one of the large groups of stars that make up the universe

Use the words in the box at the top of the page to complete the sentences.

6. Scientists have made many _____ about other planets.

7. I wonder how many stars are in those _____.

8. Rachel and her father used a _____ to look at the stars.

9. The Northern Lights were a _____ before scientists understood what caused them.

10. Someday I would like to be an astronaut and travel to another _____.

Unit 6 • Reading 2

Vocabulary

Academic Words Use with Student Edition page 320.

Read the paragraph below. Pay attention to the underlined Academic Words.

> Galileo Galilei asked many questions about how things work. He was not only a <u>philosopher</u> but also a serious scientist. He tested each <u>theory</u> using the scientific method. With his improved telescope, he <u>identified</u> the moons around Jupiter. Galileo also saw that Earth's movements were <u>predictable</u>. He discovered that the sun does not change its location, but that Earth travels around the sun.

Match each word with its definition.

Example: __d__ identified

_____ 1. philosopher

_____ 2. predictable

_____ 3. theory

a. usual, expected, or obvious

b. an idea that tries to explain something, but it may or may not be true

c. a person who studies life and what it means, how we should live, and what knowledge is

d. knew; recognized

Use the Academic Words from the exercise above to complete the sentences.

4. My father is very _____, so I always know what he is going to do.

5. I _____ the butterfly by its unusual markings.

6. The _____ spent his time reading about different things and thinking about life.

7. When a scientist has a _____, he or she has to prove that it is true.

Complete the sentences with your own ideas.

8. One thing that is predictable about me is _____.

9. An interesting theory is _____.

10. I was surprised when scientists identified _____.

Name _____ Date _____

Word Study — Spelling Long *i* Use with Student Edition page 321.

REMEMBER The long *i* sound can be spelled several different ways. These include *i_e* as in *wide*, *igh* as in *tight*, *ie* as in *pie*, and *y* as in *why*.

Read the words in the box below. Then write each word in the correct column in the chart.

like	fight	die	lightning	spy	my
dime	fry	ride	tried	lie	fried
cry	line	frighten	delight		

Words with the long *i* spelled *i_e*	Words with the long *i* spelled *igh*	Words with the long *i* spelled *ie*	Words with the long *i* spelled *y*
like			

Write the sound-spelling pattern in each word below.

Example: bright <u>long i spelled igh</u>

1. dice _____

2. might _____

3. tie _____

4. sly _____

5. mice _____

Unit 6 • Reading 2

Reading Strategy | **Evaluate New Information**

Use with Student Edition page 321.

> **REMEMBER** Evaluate new information by comparing it to information and ideas that you already know.

Read the passages. Underline information that is new to you. Then answer the questions.

1. The galaxy in which our solar system and Earth are located is called the Milky Way. Scientists believe that it contains 200 to 400 billion stars. The oldest stars in the Milky Way are thought to be about 13.2 billion years old.

   How does this new information fit into what you already know?

   _____

2. The Milky Way's name comes from the hazy white light that can be seen from Earth. The light is made up of stars and other material. The Greek philosopher Democritus is thought to be the first person to say that the Milky Way is made up of faraway stars.

   How does this new information fit into what you already know?

   _____

3. Scientists call the shape of the Milky Way a barred spiral galaxy. There is a bar-shaped area in the center. Around that there is a disk-shaped area made up of gas, dust, and stars.

   How does this new information fit into what you already know?

   _____

4. Many myths explain the formation of the Milky Way. A Greek myth says that the Milky Way was created by the milk the goddess Hera spilled as she nursed baby Heracles.

   How does this new information fit into what you already know?

   _____

5. In most places, the Milky Way is hard to see. Street lights, buildings, and cars make it too bright to see the Milky Way in cities. If you go out in the country where the sky is very dark, you will see the Milky Way's soft glow.

   How does this new information fit into what you already know?

   _____

Name _____ Date _____

Comprehension Use with Student Edition page 326.

Choose the best answer for each item. Circle the letter of the correct answer.

1. People learned to tell time, count days, predict seasons, and tell direction by studying the _____.

   a. stars b. Earth c. moon

2. Ancient Greeks discovered that some of the bright objects in the sky were actually _____.

   a. fairies b. planets c. moons

3. Al-Sufi located and identified over 1,000 _____.

   a. planets b. stars c. galaxies

4. Copernicus believed that Earth moved around the sun in a perfect _____.

   a. square b. triangle c. circle

5. Galileo discovered Jupiter's _____.

   a. moons b. suns c. lakes

Extension Use with Student Edition page 327.

Write a paragraph listing five things about astronomy or space that you would like to learn more about. Then tell where you would look to learn about these things.

_____
_____
_____
_____
_____

Unit 6 • Reading 2

Grammar: Participial Adjectives: Formation and Meaning

Use with Student Edition page 328.

> **REMEMBER** Participial adjectives end in *-ed* or *-ing*. Those ending in *-ed*, such as *surprised*, describe how a person feels. Those ending in *-ing*, such as *surprising*, describe the cause of a feeling.

Complete the sentences with the correct form of the participial adjectives in parentheses.

Example: (disturbed/disturbing) The movie was weird and ___disturbing___.

1. (annoyed/annoying) The child's constant crying was _____.

2. (confused/confusing) The student was _____ and asked the teacher to explain the lesson.

3. (surprised/surprising) The novel's ending was _____.

4. (amused/amusing) The comedy was _____.

5. (bored/boring) I was _____ at the picnic without my friends.

Write sentences with participial adjectives. Follow the directions in parentheses.

Example: (Describe how a person feels; form an adjective from *please*.)
   I was pleased that I'd passed the test.

6. (Describe the cause of a feeling; form an adjective from *amaze*.)
   _____

7. (Describe how a person feels; form an adjective from *frighten*.)
   _____

8. (Describe the cause of a feeling; form an adjective from *shock*.)
   _____

9. (Describe the cause of a feeling; form an adjective from *thrill*.)
   _____

10. (Describe how a person feels; form an adjective from *relax*.)
    _____

Name _____ Date _____

Prepositions and Infinitives with Participial Adjectives
Use with Student Edition page 329.

> **REMEMBER** Many participial adjectives ending in *-ed* are followed by specific prepositions. These include *moved by, interested in, tired of,* and *fascinated with*. These adjectival phrases have their own meaning, which can be different from the adjective by itself. Use the context to figure out their meaning or look them up in a dictionary.
>
> Many participial adjectives that end in *-ed* can also be followed by infinitives. These adjectives include *surprised, excited, amazed,* and *disappointed*. These are often adjectives that express emotion.

Underline the adjectival phrase (participial adjective + preposition OR participial adjective + infinitive) in each sentence. Then use the context to figure out its meaning. Choose the letter that best expresses the general meaning of the sentence. Use a dictionary if necessary.

Example: I was pleased with myself that I did so well on the test.

   ⓐ I felt happy.   b. I didn't feel happy.

1. Jackie was surprised by my age. She'd thought I was younger.

   a. She had known how old I was.   b. She hadn't known how old I was.

2. Steve is fascinated with robots. He's been in the robotics club since fourth grade.

   a. He doesn't like robots.   b. He likes robots a lot.

3. I was excited to hear that it's going to snow. I can't wait for a snow day!

   a. I don't want it to snow.   b. I really want it to snow.

4. Alice isn't very interested in sports. She'd rather spend time reading.

   a. She likes sports a lot.   b. She doesn't like sports very much.

5. I was shocked to hear that he'd won. I was sure the other candidate would win.

   a. I thought he would win.   b. I didn't think he'd win.

Unit 6 • Reading 2

Writing Write a Paragraph with a Main Idea and Supporting **Details** *Use with Student Edition pages 330–331.*

Complete your own word web for a paragraph to be included in a research report. List the main idea along with facts and details that support it.

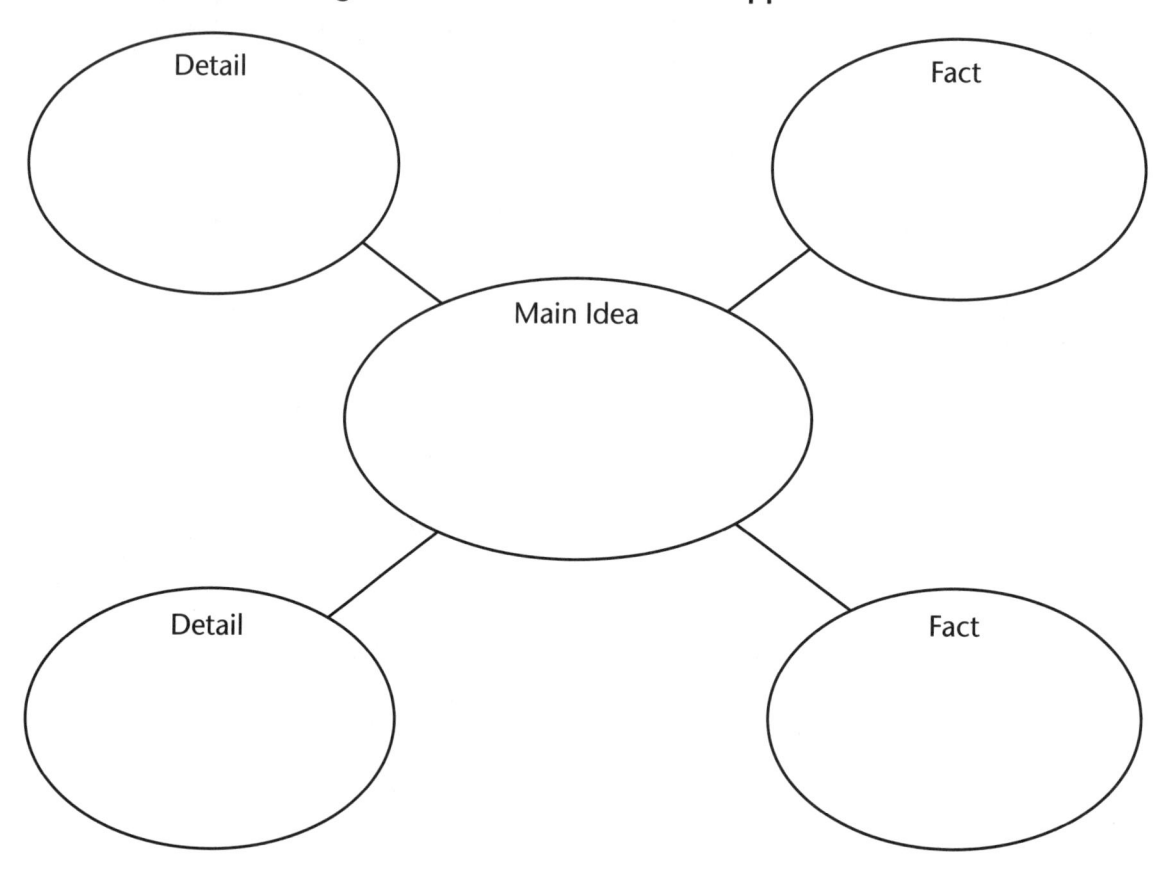

Detail

Fact

Main Idea

Detail

Fact

Have your partner complete (✓) the Peer Review Checklist. Use this feedback to help you edit your final draft.

Peer Review Checklist
- ☐ Does the paragraph present a main idea?
- ☐ Is the main idea supported by facts and details?
- ☐ Is information provided in an order that makes sense?
- ☐ Does the writing voice show understanding of the topic?
- ☐ Are participial adjectives used correctly?
- ☐ Could changes be made to improve the paragraph?

Name _____ Date _____

UNIT 6 — How do we know what is true?

Reading 3: "Proving Innocence: A Matter of Life and Death"

Vocabulary — Key Words *Use with Student Edition page 333.*

Write each word in the box next to its definition.

accurate	confessed	DNA	eyewitnesses	identify	testify

Example: ____DNA____ : a substance in the cells of your body that carries genetic information

1. _____ : say in a court of law what you know about something

2. _____ : told someone that you have done something wrong

3. _____ : correct in every detail

4. _____ : say who someone is or what something is

5. _____ : people who have seen a crime or an accident

Use the words in the box at the top of the page to complete the sentences.

6. The police couldn't find _____ to the accident, so they are not sure what happened.

7. She didn't want to _____ because she didn't see exactly how the accident happened.

8. Jake _____ to the crime after he found out the police had a video that showed him there.

9. All of the information about the crime in the article was _____.

10. Some people get _____ tests to see if they carry certain diseases.

Unit 6 • Reading 3

Vocabulary — **Academic Words** Use with Student Edition page 334.

Read the paragraph below. Pay attention to the underlined Academic Words.

> Getting new legislation approved in government is often hard to do. People have different ideas about what is important. Some people want to spend whatever money is needed to do something they support. Others want specific information about how much everything is going to cost before they make decisions. Then, there is a special procedure for voting. In general, it is an interesting, but complex, process.

Match each word with its definition.

Example: __b__ legislation   a. detailed and exact

_____ 1. procedure   b. a law or set of laws

_____ 2. complex   c. the correct or normal way of doing something

_____ 3. specific   d. complicated

Use the Academic Words from the paragraph to complete the sentences.

4. You need to follow the _____ for setting up your new computer.

5. In a court, lawyers ask _____ questions so they can get the right information.

6. The city government is going to approve new _____ to give more money to the schools.

7. The study of DNA is very _____, so scientists have to be very careful.

Complete the sentences with your own ideas.

8. A good idea for new legislation is _____.

9. One procedure that is hard for me to understand is _____.

10. I have very specific opinions about _____.

Name _____ Date _____

Word Study — Root Words *Use with Student Edition page 335.*

REMEMBER Many English words have Greek and Latin roots. For example, if you look at the word *biology*, *bio-* is a Greek root meaning *life*, and *-logy* is a Greek root meaning *expression* or *study*.

Look at the chart. Write the definitions of the words. Check your work in a dictionary.

Root	Meaning	Word	Definition
Example: carn-	meat	carnivore	meat eater
1. dict-	say	dictate	
2. brev-	short	brevity	
3. ann-	yearly	anniversary	
4. -ject	throw	reject	
5. scrib-	write	scribble	

Look at the chart. Use the roots to figure out the meaning of the words. Check a dictionary if needed.

Root	Meaning	Word	Definition
Example: fact-	make	factory	place where things are made
6. dict-		dictator	
7. brev-		abbreviation	
8. ann-		annual	
9. -ject		project	
10. -scribe		inscribe	

Unit 6 • Reading 3   179

Reading Strategy Evaluate Written Information

Use with Student Edition page 335.

> **REMEMBER** Evaluating written information helps you understand the argument the author is making.

Read the paragraph below. Then answer the questions.

> You inherit about 80,000 genes from your parents. All 80,000 genes are present in each individual cell of your body. These genes contain the instructions that make you human.
>
> DNA is like a long, twisted ladder. The rungs of the ladder have a unique pattern of genes for each person. This arrangement of genes is what makes human beings different from one another. In 1984, Sir Alec Jeffreys discovered how to make a DNA fingerprint. He took pieces of DNA and marked them with a radioactive substance. Then he made images of these DNA fragments on X-ray film. When he developed the pictures, he was surprised to see long strings of images arranged in patterns that looked a lot like the bar codes we see on products in supermarkets.

1. What is the purpose in reading this text? What type of article or literature is this? _____

2. What was the author's purpose for writing this text? Does the information consist of facts, opinions, or both? _____

3. Does the information appear to be accurate? Are trusted sources quoted? _____

4. Are the arguments or main ideas supported by evidence? _____

5. How can the strategy of evaluating written information help you understand what you read? _____

Name _____ Date _____

Comprehension *Use with Student Edition page 340.*

Choose the best answer for each item. Circle the letter of the correct answer.

1. _____ talked to the police. They said Timothy was home the day of the crime.

    a. Eyewitnesses **b.** Only a few people **c.** Timothy and a few people

2. Juries often think that crime victims will _____ their attacker.

    a. want to talk to **b.** remember **c.** forget

3. It is best for police to use DNA evidence _____ to get information about a crime.

    a. and eyewitnesses **b.** and juries **c.** only

4. The Innocence Project was started by _____.

    a. crime victims and the police **b.** innocent people in jail **c.** lawyers and students

5. The Innocence Project helps _____.

    a. people on trial **b.** people in jail **c.** crime victims

Extension *Use with Student Edition page 341.*

Write a paragraph about a crime case you know about. What kinds of evidence did the police have? Did they use DNA evidence? Do you think everybody knows the truth about what happened?

_____
_____
_____
_____
_____
_____
_____

Unit 6 • Reading 3

Grammar — Future for Prediction *Use with Student Edition page 342.*

REMEMBER Use *will* or *won't (will not)* + the base form of a verb to talk about the future. Also use *will* or *won't* + the base form of a verb to make predictions about the future. If you are not quite sure of a prediction, add *probably.* If you are even less sure, use *maybe.*

Complete the sentences with phrases from the box.

| maybe we will hear | they probably won't stay | we won't go |
| he will probably laugh | maybe we won't see | |

1. It is already raining, so _____ to the park.

2. The man is smiling, so _____ soon.

3. Our guests are tired, so _____ much longer.

4. _____ the dog barking tonight.

5. It is cloudy, so _____ any stars tonight.

Complete the predictions with the verbs in parentheses. Use *will* if the predictions will happen. Use *won't* if they will not happen. Add *probably* where noted.

Example: (maybe snow) It is getting cold and cloudy, so ___maybe___ it ___will snow___ soon.

6. (probably rain) Take an umbrella because it _____ today.

7. (probably win) We _____ the baseball game if we practice.

Write predictions with the verbs in parentheses. Use *will* if the predictions will happen. Use *won't* if they will not happen. Add *probably* or *maybe* where noted.

Example: (probably play) _I love chess, so I probably will play a game tonight_.

8. (probably watch) _____.

9. (be) _____.

10. (maybe go) _____.

Name _____ Date _____

Modals of Possibility and Advice
Use with Student Edition page 343.

> **REMEMBER** When offering a suggestion or giving advice that you don't feel very strongly about, use *could* or *might* + the base form of the verb. Use *should* or *should not* (*shouldn't*) + the base form of the verb when you feel more strongly. Use *have to*, *must*, or *must not* + the base form of the verb when you feel very strongly.

Choose the best word or phrase to complete the conversation.

Doug: Allie, I need some advice. Should I get my driver's license this year?

Allie: I don't know. You just got your learner's permit. You _____*could*_____ wait another year.
could / have to

Doug: I know, but I'm sick of walking everywhere.

Allie: I understand, but I still think you _____ wait
must / should

until you get more practice. I'm going to wait until I'm 20.

Doug: No way! You can get your license now! You absolutely

_____ get your license this year!
could / have to

Allie: You seem awfully sure that that's the best thing. I think it's better to wait. You

_____ rush into it. You
couldn't / shouldn't

_____ be sorry later.
might / should

Doug: Well, you _____ be right. Thanks, Allie.
could / must

Unit 6 • Reading 3

Grammar Punctuation of Direct Quotations

Use with Student Edition page 344.

> **REMEMBER** A **direct quotation** is a speaker's exact words. It is enclosed in quotation marks. When a phrase such as *he said* or *she said* is used with a direct quotation, the speech is separated from the phrase by a comma.
> **Example:** "Don't go in there," she said.
> When *he said* or *she said* is used before a direct quotation, the speech begins with a capital letter.
> **Example:** As she came in the door, they said, "Welcome."

Put a ✓ next to the sentence in each pair that is correctly punctuated and capitalized.

Example: ___✓___ "Watch a news broadcast tonight," our teacher said.
_____ Watch a news broadcast tonight" our teacher said.

_____ 1. "Lets watch the news," she said.
_____   "Let's watch the news," She said.

_____ 2. The announcer said "Today, all the news is bad."
_____   The announcer said, "Today, all the news is bad."

_____ 3. "The candidates will hold a debate tonight," The newscaster said.
_____   "The candidates will hold a debate tonight," the newscaster said.

_____ 4. The weatherman said, "it will rain tomorrow."
_____   The weatherman said, "It will rain tomorrow."

_____ 5. "Take an umbrella with you," he advised.
_____   "Take an umbrella with you" he advised.

Correctly punctuate the sentences. In addition, circle all letters that should be capitalized, and draw a line through all letters that should not be capitalized.

Example: He said, "(y)esterday's science fiction is often today's science."

6. I read the news online The student said.

7. The teacher explained the reading is based on a real news story.

8. I said no one believes that man is innocent.

9. she said If you are well informed, you can make good decisions.

10. He said we didn't believe that story.

Name _____ Date _____

Quoting Sources *Use with Student Edition page 345.*

> **REMEMBER** To quote a source in a research paper, you can use a direct quotation. The direct quotation is set off with quotation marks and begins with a capital letter. If you do not need to quote all of the quotation, you can use only part of it. Since it is not a complete sentence, the phrase should begin with a lowercase letter, unless it is a proper noun, which is always capitalized.
> You can also quote a source using reported speech. Don't forget that quotation marks are not used and that verbs and pronouns often change. When reporting a fact, as you often do in research papers, the verb form does not have to change.

Follow the instructions below to quote the sources.

Example: Use reported speech: "Education is not preparation for life; education is life itself." –John Dewey

John Dewey stated that education is not preparation for life, but that education is life itself.

1. Use a direct quote: "Every man dies. Not every man really lives." –William Wallace

   _____.

2. Use reported speech: "The biggest adventure you can take is to live the life of your dreams." –Oprah Winfrey

   _____.

3. Use the underlined phrase in a quote: "It is crucial to make <u>one's own writing circle</u>." –Naomi Shihab Nye

   _____.

4. Use a direct quote: "We're drowning in information and starving for knowledge." –Rutherford D. Rogers

   _____.

5. Use reported speech: "Biologists think that some animals use the position of the sun and stars to help tell where they are going." –Darlene R. Stille

   _____.

Unit 6 • Reading 3

Writing — **Write a Paragraph with Quotations and Citations**

Use with Student Edition pages 346–347.

Complete your own word web for a paragraph for a research report. List your quotations and citations in the web.

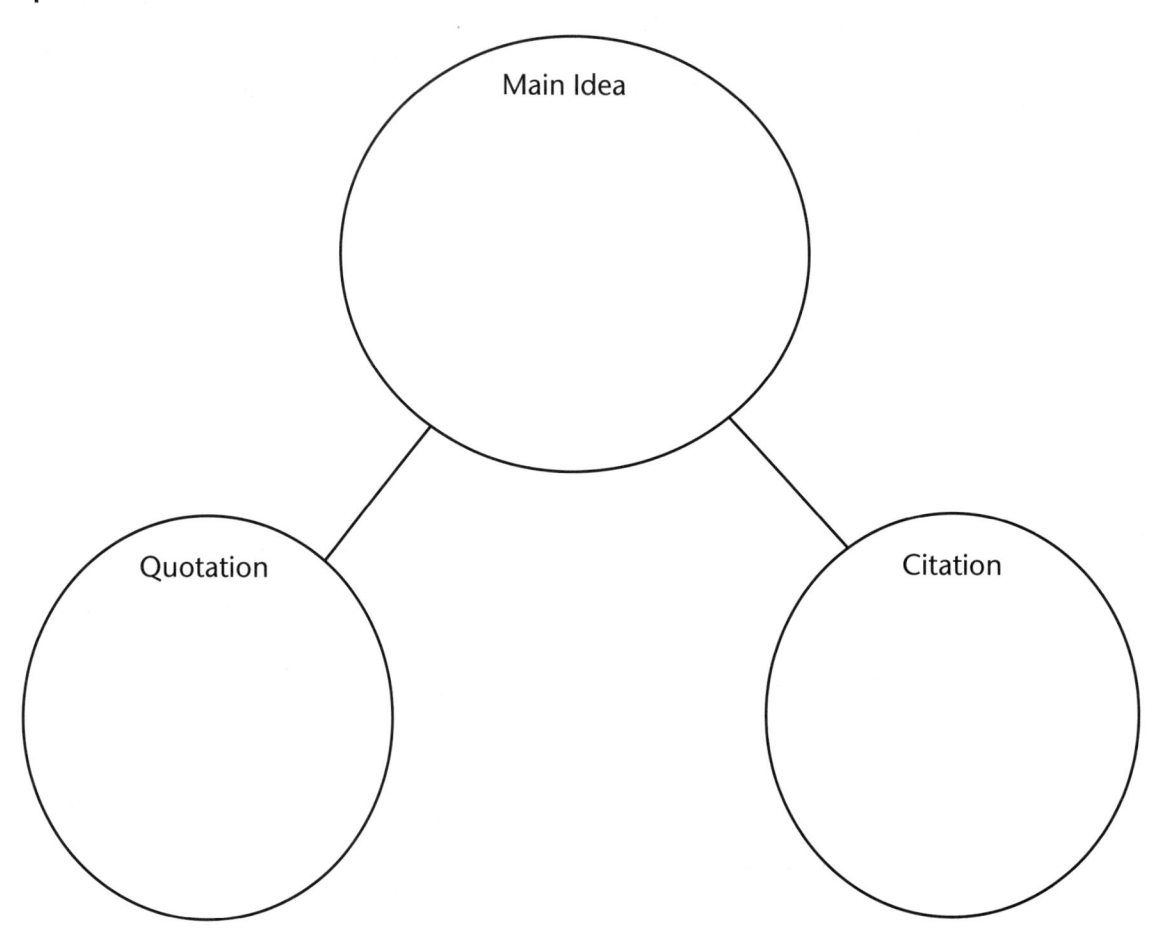

- Main Idea
- Quotation
- Citation

Have your partner complete (✓) the Peer Review Checklist. Use this feedback to help you edit your final draft.

Peer Review Checklist

- ☐ Does the paragraph present a main idea?
- ☐ Does it include at least one quotation and citation?
- ☐ Do all quotations support the main idea?
- ☐ Are all quotations punctuated correctly?
- ☐ Are all citations accurate and complete?
- ☐ Could changes be made to improve the paragraph?

Name _____ Date _____

Writing Workshop *Use with Student Edition pages 352–356.*

Organize your ideas in the graphic organizer below.

I.
  A.
  B.
II.
  A.
  B.
III.
  A.
  B.
IV.
  A.
  B.
V.
  A.
  B.

Have your partner complete (✓) the Peer Review Checklist. Use this feedback to help you edit your final draft.

Peer Review Checklist
- ☐ Did the report provide information and explanations?
- ☐ Did the first paragraph introduce a controlling idea?
- ☐ Was the organization of facts and details easy to follow?
- ☐ Did the writer vary sentence lengths and patterns?
- ☐ Were words spelled correctly?
- ☐ Could changes be made to improve the report?

Learning Log *Use after completing Student Edition page 358.*

Underline the vocabulary items you know and can use well. Review and practice any you haven't underlined. Underline them when you know them well.

Literary Words	Key Words	Academic Words	
myth hero heroine	constellations discoveries galaxy phenomenon solar system telescope accurate confessed DNA eyewitnesses identify testify	evaluate infer manipulate role identified philosopher predictable theory	complex legislation procedure specific

Put a check by the skills you can perform well. Review and practice any you haven't checked off. Check them off when you can perform them well.

Skills	I can . . .
Word Study	☐ recognize and use antonyms. ☐ recognize and spell words with the long *i*. ☐ recognize and use root words.
Reading Strategies	☐ compare and contrast. ☐ evaluate new information. ☐ evaluate written information.
Grammar	☐ use reported speech in statements and questions. ☐ use the past progressive with adverbial clauses. ☐ use participial adjectives. ☐ use prepositions and infinitives with participial adjectives. ☐ use the future to make predictions. ☐ use modals to express possibility. ☐ punctuate direct quotations correctly. ☐ use quoted sources correctly.
Writing	☐ write an introductory paragraph. ☐ write a paragraph with a main idea and supporting details. ☐ write a paragraph with quotations and citations. ☐ write a research report.

Test Preparation

Test 1

DIRECTIONS
Read this selection. Then answer the questions that follow it.

Big Bend National Park

(1) Welcome to Big Bend National Park! (2) You will find many different campgrounds available to meet your needs. (3) Please feel free to ask the park ranger any questions you have about your stay. (4) Feed the birds before you leave.

(5) There are five campgrounds in the park. (6) All have toilets, but only two have electricity. (7) You can go to Chisos Basin for rustic camping. (8) If you have a recreational vehicle, you can go to the Rio Grande Village RV Park. (9) Hear, you'll have all of the comforts of home.

1. What change, if any, should be made to sentence 9?
   A. Change *Hear* to **Here**
   B. Change *you'll* to **yawl**
   C. Delete the comma
   D. Make no change

2. Which sentence does NOT belong in the passage?
   A. Sentence 1
   B. Sentence 4
   C. Sentence 6
   D. Sentence 8

Test 2

DIRECTIONS
Read this selection. Then answer the questions that follow it.

> Craig wrote this report about bats. His science teacher asked him to find out if what people believed about bats was true. Craig would like you to read his rough draft and suggest corrections and improvements he should make.

Bats: Myths and Facts

(1) Many popular beliefs about bats are false. (2) Bats are mammals, like us. (3) They are not rodents, like mice and rats. (4) Bats are not blind. (5) They are used to seeing at night and some species see very well. (6) They do not try to get into people's hair. (7) If you're outside and have mosquitoes around your head, the bat is aimed only for the mosquitoes, not for your head. (8) Of about 900 species of bats, only three species of vampire bats drink the blood of large mamals. (9) Bats do carry rabies. (10) They don't carry it any more than other kinds of wild animals do.

1. What change, if any, should be made in sentence 5?
   A Add a comma after *night*
   B Change *to seeing* to *to saw*
   C Change *are* to *is*
   D Make no change

2. What revision should be made in sentence 7?
   A Change *you're* to *your*
   B Change the period to a question mark
   C Change *aimed* to *aiming*
   D Remove the commas

3. What change, if any, should be made in sentence 8?
   A Remove the comma
   B Change *vampire bats* to **Vampire Bats**
   C Change *mamals* to **mammals**
   D Make no change

4. What is the BEST way to combine sentences 9 and 10?
   A Bats do carry rabies, and they don't carry it any more than other kinds of wild animals do.
   B Bats do carry rabies; but they don't carry it any more than other kinds of wild animals do.
   C Bats do carry rabies and they don't carry it any more than other kinds of wild animals do.
   D Bats do carry rabies, but they don't carry it any more than other kinds of wild animals do.

Test 3

DIRECTIONS
Read this selection. Then answer the questions that follow it.

Anna wrote this report about the effect of cars on Americans for her social studies class. Anna would like you to read her rough draft and suggest corrections and improvements she should make.

Automobiles in America

(1) When Henry Ford started making cars, he wanted ordinary people to be able to buys them. (2) He made cars using an assembly line. (3) This made cars cheaper. (4) Then many people were able to buy cars. (5) This meant that they could move around a lot. (6) They could travel and saw new places. (7) They could also live in a different place from where they worked. (8) That's why suburbs grew around cities.

(9) The automobile industry created jobs for many people, which is good for the economy. (10) People could find work at car factories and also at the new businesses that began because of cars, such as gas stations, repair shops, and car lots. (11) Cars meant that roads and highways has to be built, and that led to more jobs for people, too.

(12) Even though there were many advantages, the car industry also brought new problems. (13) Once there were roads and highways, people could travel easily. (14) Trucks could move goods from one place to another. (15) But the large number of cars on the roads creates noise and air pollution. (16) We continue to deal with this problem now.

(17) Today the automobile is still the main way people get around every day. (18) Everywhere you look, there are highways, big parking lots, and drive-through windows. (19) With its positive and negative effects, the automobile has changed our economy. (20) It has changed our lives.

1. What change, if any, should be made in sentence 1?
   A Remove the comma
   B Change *buys* to **buy**
   C Changed *started* to **starting**
   D Make no change

2. What revision should be made in sentence 6?
   A Change the period to a question mark
   B Change *saw* to **see**
   C Change *could travel* to **should travel**
   D Remove the comma

3. What change, if any, should be made in sentence 9?
   A Change *which* to **what**
   B Change *is* to **was**
   C Change *created* to **creating**
   D Make no change

4. What revision should be made in sentence 11?
   A Change *too* to **to**
   B Change *has* to **had**
   C Change *built* to **builts**
   D Change *led* to **lead**

5. What change, if any, should be made in sentence 15?
   A Change *creates* to **created**
   B Change *pollution* to **polution**
   C Add a comma
   D Make no change

6. What is the BEST way to combine sentences 19 and 20?
   A With its positive and negative effects, the automobile has changed our economy; and it has changed our lives.
   B With its positive and negative effects, the automobile has changed our economy, but it has changed our lives.
   C With its positive and negative effects, the automobile has changed our economy and our lives.
   D With its positive and negative effects, the automobile has changed our economy but it has changed our lives.

Name _____ Date _____

Visual Literacy: Smithsonian American Art Museum
Use with Student Edition pages 360–361.

Learning to Look

Look at *Angel* by Abbott Handerson Thayer on page 360 of your Student Edition. Describe four things you see in this painting. State facts, not opinions.

Example: *I see wings.*

1. _____
2. _____
3. _____
4. _____

Interpretation

Look at *Arachne* by Bruce Conner on page 361 in your Student Edition. How would you describe this painting to someone who had never seen it? Write a story about it.

Example: *I see many different types of materials and colors. . . .*

_____
_____
_____
_____
_____
_____
_____
_____
_____
_____

Compare & Contrast

Look at *Arachne* by Bruce Conner on page 361 in your Student Edition and *Angel* by Abbott Handerson Thayer on page 360 in your Student Edition. How are these two artworks similar?

Example: The artists used paint in both artworks.

How are they different?

Editing and Proofreading Marks

To:	Use This Mark	Example:
add something	∧	We ate rice, bean︵s and corn.
delete something	˞	We ate rice, beans, and corns.
close space	‿	We ‿ ate rice, beans, and corn.
start a new paragraph	¶	¶ We ate rice, beans, and corn.
add a comma	⍦	We ate rice, beans and corn.
add a period	⊙	We ate rice, beans, and corn⊙
switch letters or words	∽	We ate rice, baens, and corn.
change to a capital letter	a̲̲	we ate rice, beans, and corn.
change to a lowercase letter	⌿	WE ate rice, beans, and corn.
let the marked text stand	(stet)	We ate rice, beans, and corn. (stet)

Additional Editing and Proofreading Practice

Read the paragraph below carefully. Look for mistakes in spelling, punctuation, and grammar. Mark the mistakes with proofreader's marks. Then rewrite the paragraph correctly on the lines below.

> my mom said that I had to cleen my bedroom. It was a Saturday, and I wanted to go outside and be with my friends. She said that I could go Out as soon I was done. First, I made my bed. I put away all my clothes. I found some old clothes, in my closet. I decided to give them to my little sisters. I also found a book of beautiful old stamps. They was a gift from my grandmother. She gave them to me when I was a baby little. Under my bed I saw my favorite toy. It is a blue cool model train. I am glad i cleaned my room! I'll show the train to my friends.

Additional Editing and Proofreading Practice   **197**

Edit and Proofread

Read the paragraph below carefully. Look for mistakes in spelling, punctuation, and grammar. Mark the mistakes with proofreader's marks. Then rewrite the paragraph correctly on the lines below.

> Maybe it was the fresh air that made Boris so drowsy. maybe it was the fact that the class was held after lunch. Whatever the reason. Boris fell asleep in algebra class again today. Michele couldn't resist playing a trik on her friend. She tickled his fingers just enough to wake him up. The next thing she knew, Boris woke with a start and was screaming. Michele knowed she had made a terrible mistake, cuz the other students began to laugh at her freind

Edit and Proofread

Read the paragraph below carefully. Look for mistakes in spelling, punctuation, and grammar. Mark the mistakes with proofreader's marks. Then rewrite the paragraph correctly on the lines below.

> Lisa was planing a party she was inviting all her friends. What should she buy for her party? Lisa made a list of everything she needed she decided to get a lot of pretzels and juice. Then she thought she would by potatochips and maybe some ice cream for desert. If her friends got hungry, she could always order several pizzas. It was summer, so lisa decided not to cook anything for her friends eat. Lisa thought, maybe she would make a salad. Everyone likes salad in the summer? Lisa was sure her party would be a lot of fun. She telphoned all her friends to ask them to come.

Additional Editing and Proofreading Practice

199

Edit and Proofread

Read the paragraph below carefully. Look for mistakes in spelling, punctuation, and grammar. Mark the mistakes with proofreader's marks. Then rewrite the paragraph correctly on the lines below.

as I began my walk to school, the clouds were beginning to form. When I was a block away from my house, I felt the first raindrop I looked in my backpak. Their was no umbrella. It started to rain harder. I started to run. I herd a loud clap of thunder. i ran faster. My legs were pumping underneath me. My face was soaked with the warm, spring rain. I ran past cars trees, people and houses. I felt great! I saw my best friend maggie riding by on the bus. I waved and shouted out her name as I sped past. I saw a big puddle ahead. I tried to stop in time, but – SPLAT! I fell in the puddle I was soaked. What a way to start my first day of school!

Edit and Proofread

Read the paragraph below carefully. Look for mistakes in spelling, punctuation, and grammar. Mark the mistakes with proofreader's marks. Then rewrite the paragraph correctly on the lines below.

> Today, the West is one of the fastest growing areas in the united states. Many people are moving to California Arizona and New Mexico Lots of people move out West for the good Weather. They think everyone spends all day outdors in the sunshine. it is true that parts of these states are deserts and get little rain. Yet northern California recieves lots of rain. It is much wetter than southern California. Moving to Arizona or New Mexico if you want to avoid rain.

Additional Editing and Proofreading Practice

Edit and Proofread

Read the paragraph below carefully. Look for mistakes in spelling, punctuation, and grammar. Mark the mistakes with proofreader's marks. Then rewrite the paragraph correctly on the lines below.

Im so excited to be spending time with my Family this weekend. We plan to go camping, and the thing I'm looking forward to the most is stargazing. to avoid the city lights, we will drive out to the country where it is very dark. There we will spred out our blankets, lie on our backs, and look up at the sky. I'm going to bring my telascope, which will help us look for the Milky way and the Big Dipper. I got a book form the library that shows many different constellation and where to look for them. i'm hoping we will see a shooting star, too